KB075703

DR.DENEN
Connecting The Dots

YONGBEOM KIM

DR. DENEN: CONNECTING THE DOTS

발 행|2024년 2월 6일
저 자|김용범
펴낸이|한건희
펴낸곳|주식회사 부크크
출판사등록|2014.07.15.(제2014-16호)
주 소|서울특별시 금천구 가산디지털1로 119 SK트윈타워 A동
305호
전 화|1670-8316
이메일|info@bookk.co.kr

ISBN|979-11-410-7044-1

www.bookk.co.kr

Table of Contents

What is The Principle That Leads The Universe?

Epilogue 1

Epilogue 2

Prologue

1. Cheering for the Wounded

People who have endured hardships and achieved success in their youth are often strict with themselves, but even more so with others. Their attitude is like, "I went through all this hardship to learn, how can you not manage this?" This leads them to push others even harder, sometimes even trying to teach them, and in extreme cases, causing harm.

I was like this too. Falling into this kind of error puts one's life in a constant state of tension, which is distressing. That's why I believe people like me, who have this mindset, especially need the ability to empathize with others. Similarly, those who are deeply wounded themselves are more likely to be harsh with others, rather than supportive. I mention this in the prologue because my following writings might seem to reflect this attitude. Additionally, my writings are a form of projection, essentially speaking to my own inadequacies. Thus, I suggest you take my writings merely as a reference, or even disregard them as the ramblings of an old fuddy-duddy.

Everyone in this world carries their own wounds. The bride and groom at a wedding, looking blissfully happy, and those who are envied for their success, all have their own struggles if you look closely. That's why I believe we should understand

and support each other, including ourselves, who are all wounded in our own ways.

Yongbeom Kim
On the last day of 2023
From Ui-Am Medical Center

The First Dot: Yanagita

He was an exceedingly peculiar individual, appearing too extraordinary to be considered ordinary and too ordinary to be deemed extraordinary. His visit occurred around late September, a time of occasional light showers but gradually decreasing humidity, offering pleasant weather.

**

Living my entire life without ever leaving the vicinity of Dōjinmachi Station, I harbored no grand ambitions or special desires in life. For me, each day was the epitome of ordinariness. If there was any indulgence I sought, it was to end my days at 'Hiro,' a yakitori shop frequently visited in my neighborhood, enjoying beer. Although there might be hundreds of yakitori places in Fukuoka, in areas like Hakata Station, Tenjin, or Nakasu, the only one I cared for was 'Hiro,' identifiable by its red signboard.

I believe in drinking just enough to feel the buzz, but on some days, I end up slightly more inebriated, invariably after encountering people at Hiro who are clueless about the proper way to enjoy yakitori. Occasionally, I see patrons removing the skewered chicken and placing it into a separate dish. In my view, they are not purists. If one intends to eat it off a plate, why skewer the chicken in the first place? Yakitori is too refined for those who either ignore tradition or live whimsically according to their tastes. Most people who loudly advocate for respecting personal preferences usually lack the sophistication to have preferences worth respecting.

***

My initial impression of Mr. Denen was like seeing yakitori half-transferred to a plate indecisive. His purpose was clear, but my response to him was ambiguous. The first time I heard of Mr. Denen was through a phone call from a stranger.

"Moshi moshi, is this Mr. Yanagita?"
"Yes, it is. May I ask who's calling?"
"Hello, I am Makoto Kakegawa, the secretary general of KMP Group."
"Ah, yes. What can I do for KMP Group's secretary office?"
"Do you happen to own land near Dojinmachi Station?"
"Yes, I do. But how did you come to know of this?"
"My apologies for the intrusion, but our chairman, Mr. Denen, is seeking a suitable location for a special project and happened upon your property. I apologize again if this is an inconvenience."
"It's not an inconvenience, but I'm curious what interest KMP Group could have in this quiet place."
In the Japanese real estate industry, there's a widely known saying that only three out of a thou-

sand words are true. I remember that KMP Group started from real estate and has now become a conglomerate, but I couldn't help feeling distrustful. My guess was that reaching such a corporate height in real estate must have involved 'kakoi komi' (encircling) business practices, which means monopolizing information and charging commissions from both sides. This approach, in my view, was as distasteful as overcharging on top of already high fees. Just like the sight of skewered yakitori piled high on a plate, there's something in the real estate business that I simply can't stomach. It's a certain point of principle for me, a mix of stubbornness and belief.

"Hah, as if there are any clean rich men. I have no interest whatsoever."

I snorted in derision, careful to keep it from carrying over the phone.

"I'm sorry, but my land is not for sale. I have no need or desire to sell. Perhaps you should look elsewhere?"
"Our chairman is willing to negotiate generously, beyond the current market value. Would that still be difficult?"
"It's not about the price. I'm sorry."
"Even if you have no current plans to sell, we would appreciate your reconsideration. I apologize for contacting you by phone today and will

call again after some time to see if you've recon-sidered."

"Alright, understood."

A few days later, the secretary's office called again with a higher offer, but my mind remained un-changed.

***

"Mr. Yanagita"

It was a baffling situation. On days when my wife addressed me not with the familiar 'dear' but rather as 'Mr.', it invariably meant something was up.

"What's the story this time, calling me like that?" I asked.

"I heard something," she replied.

"What did you hear?"

"There's someone offering 100 million yen for the land. Some chairman of a group, they say?"

"Where did you hear that story?"

"I have ears and legs too. How could I not know? If someone's offering 100 million yen for land worth 50 million, we'd have to conjure up land from thin air to sell. Why are you so stubborn about not sell-ing land we rightfully own?"

"Dear, what would we do with that money at our age? It's not enough to change our lives, and a vague sale leads to a vague disappearance. It seems better to keep the land as is..."

"But you're always so stubborn, just like you insist on going to 'Hiro,' no matter your age."

"It's because it's uncertain. Uncertain!"

"It seems you're the only one who finds it uncertain. And even if it's uncertain, selling at that price is the right decision."

As I observed my wife's firm attitude, I felt a moment of disconcertment, but my thoughts remained largely unchanged. Then, unexpectedly, a call came from him.

"Hello, is this Mr. Yanagita?"

"Yes, I am Yanagita, but who might this be?"

"I'm Denen from the KMP Group. I apologize for reaching out over the phone."

"Denen? The chairman of the KMP Group, you say?"

"Yes, that's me. I apologize for any inconvenience caused by my secretary's office previously."

"Not at all. What brings you to call me directly?"

Denen's voice was slow and respectful, yet had a pleasant timbre, creating a sense of familiarity.

"I wonder if you've considered the offer I made through my secretary?"

"I'm quite decided on that matter and don't plan to change my mind."

"I urge you to reconsider with an open mind. If you decide today, I can arrange 100 million yen by tomorrow. It's a fair amount."

"The amount is sufficient, of course. I'm aware of my land's value. But it's hard for me, born and raised here, to sell to outsiders, especially a corporation. If my words seem harsh, I apologize."

"That's perfectly understandable. But after today, due to circumstances, we can only offer 50 million yen matching the market price. Your decision today would greatly help."

A hint of annoyance crept up within me. It seemed as if I appeared to him like someone trying to negotiate for a higher sale price. I needed to reject more firmly.

"I've said it's not about the price. The area around Dojinmachi, where my land is, is particularly quiet. It doesn't seem suitable for a large corporation's projects. If it's not too much trouble, may I ask what your plans for the land are?"

Denen paused before continuing.

"In my youth, I often visited a yakitori shop near Dojinmachi. I loved the area's slow pace and the food. Even then, I thought if I ever grew my family business, I'd like to spend time in such a tranquil place, reading books. Though busy, I can't reside there yet, but I feel like I'm completing a task I left unfinished in my younger days. With your permission, I'd like to build a small library on that land, a space where anyone can rest easily."

"A library?"

I was momentarily at a loss for words upon hearing Mr. Denen's unexpected reply. A library, of all things, was both an unforeseen answer and reason.

"A library? That's something I hadn't considered. It presents quite a dilemma."
"Wouldn't it be beneficial for those living nearby? Instead of thanking me for building the library, they might rather thank Mr. Yanagita."
Beside me, my wife kept urging me on, while Mr. Denen's calm breathing awaited my response over the phone.

"Mr. Denen, that's fine. However, there are two conditions. No, actually, there are three conditions."
"Yes, I'm listening. Please go ahead, and I will consider Mr. Yanagita's proposal."
"Firstly, as you mentioned, the price will be 100 million yen. I don't want to sell, but if I must find a reason to do so, it's because of a rumor that my wife heard in the neighborhood, which has put me in an awkward position. Therefore, it seems the only way to resolve my issue is to go with the price mentioned in that rumor."
I heard Mr. Denen's laughter and cough over the phone.

"The second and third are personal requests. If you ever visit Dojinmachi, you must only eat yakitori at a place called Hiro, and you must eat it right off the skewers."

This time, a louder laugh came through the phone.

"Mr. Yanagita is quite traditional. Very well, though they are challenging conditions, I will accept them all."

So, unexpectedly that night, whether impulsively or stubbornly, I decided to sell the land.

***

After that, I believe I saw Mr. Denen at Hiro. A dignified elderly gentleman with a gentle expression was leisurely dining in a corner of the restaurant. I don't know why, but I felt it was Mr. Denen. The skewers in front of him were empty, so it was unclear if he followed the traditional way of eating, but since then, the library construction had begun.

What Are We Living For?

2. What Are We Living For?

I first asked myself this question around my freshman year of high school. I started attending church with my mother when I was young and was baptized in elementary school. At that time, the Catholic Church felt like a newly popular celebrity religion. The priests, nuns, and parishioners were kind people, and it felt refreshing compared to other religions. However, my parents' influence made Catholicism feel like an obligation. This perception changed drastically in my third year of middle school when I fell ill. I suffered from juvenile rheumatoid arthritis, a rare condition at the time. The pain was so intense that I spent my three years of high school wanting to die every day. I questioned why God would inflict such pain at this point in my life and became skeptical of religion. Back then, diagnosis and treatment were difficult, but now, medical advancements have made it manageable. Eventually, my career aspiration, which I had never considered before, became to be a doctor, and I have been one ever since. During my illness, I pondered what we live for. Based on my religious beliefs from childhood and the philosophy I studied after my illness, *I concluded that the purpose of life is to die with a purer soul than when we were born.*

Key Concepts
- Let's think about the purpose of our lives while we are still young.
- Living with a purer soul than when we were born is a value worth striving for.

3. As We Grow from Birth, We Mature Both Physically and Mentally.

According to French philosopher Jacques Lacan, humans inherently desire what others desire, pursuing money, fame, and physical pleasures. However, there are limits to these pursuits. A well-known anecdote from Buddha illustrates this:

"In ancient times, a traveler was aimlessly wandering across a desolate plain when suddenly a wild elephant charged at him. Fortunately, the traveler discovered a well and escaped the danger by climbing down a vine into it. However, inside the well's wall, four venomous snakes were flicking their tongues, and at the bottom, a venomous dragon lay in wait, hoping for the traveler to fall. The traveler's only support was the vine, but even that was at risk of breaking as a white rat and a black rat alternately gnawed at it. He was greatly startled and afraid. Just then, five drops of honey fell from a tree into his mouth, tasting incredibly sweet. The traveler, in this moment of peril, forgot his dangerous predicament and indulged greedily in the taste of the honey."

In this metaphor, the traveler represents life, the desolate plain signifies ignorance, the elephant symbolizes impermanence, and the well represents the world of life and death. The vine stands for our life. The black and white rats signify the passage of day and night. The four venomous snakes represent the four great elements: earth, water, fire, and wind. The five drops of honey symbolize the five desires: wealth, sensual pleasure, food, fame, and longevity. And the venomous dragon embodies death.

Humans are such pitiable beings. *Within the finite span of our lives, we foolishly cling to material desires. What, then, is eternal? I believe it is the human heart.* The heart is the one thing we can carry with us eternally, surpassing the limits of our physical bodies. I also think that much of what happens in the human world depends on the heart. However, some situations are beyond the reach of our hearts. For instance, issues like global warming, natural disasters, and diseases cannot be completely resolved by the power of our hearts, regardless of our efforts or attitudes. Thus, the saying "everything depends on the heart" holds certain influence in situations within our control, but may not apply in others. Nevertheless, I believe that steadying our hearts and striving always leads to positive change, giving us great strength to overcome difficulties.

Key Concepts
- The only eternal thing for a human is their heart.
- Many things in the world depend on one's heart.

---

4. Everything Arises from the Mind

In Buddhism, this idea is known as "*Ilche-Yusimjo*" *(一切有心調), meaning all beings originate from the mind*. This concept asserts that all existences are influenced by the mind, and this influence determines their lives.

I have several thoughts on this concept. First, Ilche-Yusimjo is incredibly useful in understanding and interpreting human life. Since all beings originate from the mind, the notion that our actions and attitudes directly impact our lives is significant. This concept encourages self-responsibility and introspection, aiding in personal growth and improving relationships with others. Second, Ilche-Yusimjo emphasizes the interconnectedness of all beings. Our actions and attitudes interact with other beings, affecting their lives. Thus, it helps overcome egocentric thinking and view our lives from a broader perspective. Third, Ilche-Yusimjo promotes mutual respect and humanity. As other beings also originate from the mind, it underscores the need to respect and consider them. This enriches our social lives. In conclusion, Ilche-Yusimjo is a highly beneficial concept for understanding and improving our lives and relationships. It leads to a more introspective self, stronger connections with others, and a richer social life.

> Key Concept
> - Ilche-Yusimjo is a concept that permeates life.

5. The Life of Effort

If the reason for living life lies in the cultivation and dedication of the mind, how can one achieve this purpose? Personally, I practice and reflect on six methods.

The first is *the life of effort*. Effort refers to our attitude of continually striving to achieve our goals. This strengthens our perseverance and patience, offering opportunities to grow in the process of reaching our objectives. The motto of the high school I graduated from was "Sincerity, Effort, Service." I still remember these words, found in our school song, even 30 years after graduation. Back in high school, I thought of this motto as rather commonplace. But now, I realize its profound significance. Living has taught me that without sincerity and effort, one cannot cultivate the mind or achieve success. Furthermore, most of the successful and personally mature individuals I have encountered possessed the virtue of effort. I believe this to be one of the most fundamental human values. Isn't there a saying, 'If you don't go crazy, you cannot reach it'? *I truly believe that if one exerts themselves to the point of madness, there is nothing they cannot achieve.*

Key Concepts
- The first of the six methods of practice is effort.
- Let's try to endeavor to the point of madness.

---

6. Summer Vacation

Throughout my time running a hospital, I only took a summer vacation once. I recall it was the summer of 2014, when my eldest child was in the first year of high school. For me, summer vacations are best spent in the hospital. The reason being, I find hospitals to be quite cool during the summer, and personally, I'm not fond of wandering around in the heat. I consider this a rational choice. I don't feel envious or jealous of others who go on splendid vacation trips. To me, it's all about personal preference.

On summer afternoons, when the heat tends to reduce patient visits, I find myself tackling various tasks in my office, including writing, as I am doing now. This is why I often end up devising various business strategies and reading extensively during the summer. One should have their own views on vacations and leisure time. Especially in Korea, people tend to be overly conscious of others' opinions, leading to a sense of emptiness later in life, feeling they haven't lived their own life fully. Vacations should be enjoyed in a way that's comfortable for oneself. *Those who want to travel should travel, and those who prefer to work in a cool office should do so.*

Key Concept
- Enjoy your vacation in your own way.

7. Morning Commute

I always arrive at the hospital first thing in the morning. Being a morning person by nature makes this possible. I once read in a book that *luxury cars are often seen early in the morning on the roads, and that many are parked at the library at dawn.* It implies that successful people start their day early.

After arriving early, I enjoy a cup of coffee, check my emails, and usually listen to audiobooks. I like the phrase "listening to books." It's during these times, when I'm listening, that I feel most at peace. These early dawn hours are a time for recharging. In fact, I'm writing this very piece on a quiet Sunday morning in summer, sipping a cup of coffee in my room. These moments, accumulated day by day, become one's assets. It's important to do something consistently every day. I believe that even small drops of water, falling steadily, can eventually bore through rock.

Key Concepts
- Try arriving first at work and listening to a book.
- Steady, daily efforts can make even water droplets penetrate a rock.

The Second Dot: Azumi

My name 'Azumi' was derived from Azumino City in Nagano Prefecture, a place my father remembered as striking during his youth. Although my father passed away early, leaving me with scant memories of him, I remember him through the name he gave me. This memory, so incomplete, always seemed insufficient to serve as the fence around my life, the traces my father left behind.

***

Life was imperfect, but mathematics was complete. Perhaps my fascination with mathematics stemmed from its perfect beauty. People lie, but numbers do not; everything man-made is imperfect and thus not beautiful, yet pi, seemingly random, is simultaneously beautiful.

In my life, which I believed to be random yet stable, cracks began to appear outside the realm of numbers. As always, the problem was people. I had little interest in life beyond numbers, but perhaps because of this, the small math academy I started in my neighborhood had grown to a size well-known throughout the area. Starting in a corner of an old five-story building, the academy eventually needed to use all floors except the first, bustling with students. Soon, other educational institutes, including more math academies, sprang up nearby, turning the area into a student-filled street. All of this wasn't planned or expected; it was a modest beginning I hadn't anticipated. Having little interest in management or administration, I entrusted the business to a reliable manager and, with the ample income, could immerse myself deeper into the world of mathematics. Then, one ordinary day, the building owner came to see me unexpectedly.

Foreboding often amplifies through hearing, not sight. Seeing gives us the luxury of time to prepare our minds, but sudden sounds can startle us unprepared. That was how the landlord's knock sounded to me.

Knock. Knock. A mundane yet sudden sound brought a surge of tension.

"Yes, I'm here. Please come in."
"Hello, Teacher. It's Yutaka. May I come in for a moment?"
"Hello, Mr. Yutaka. What brings you here?"
Mr. Yutaka, the owner of the five-story building, was usually a quiet and relaxed man.

"Nothing special, Azumi."

It wasn't like him to visit unannounced unless it was important, so his words hinted at the significance of what was to come.

"The lease is about to expire. You know that, right?"

"Yes, I'm aware. I was informed that it would be renewed unless there were any special issues."

"Until recently, there weren't. But my son, who just returned from abroad, wants to start a business in this building."

"Your son wants to start a business here?"

"Yes, he does. He wants to open a school. I don't know much about it."

"As you know, Mr. Yutaka, our academy was the first in this area, and it's because of us that this area turned into an educational hub. What are we supposed to do if you now ask us to leave?"

"I am sorry about this. We have our circumstances, and there's nothing we can do. I can only hope for a favorable decision from you, Azumi."

"I'm a bit confused. Can I discuss this with my administrator and get back to you? I'm sorry I can't offer you a cup of tea right now, I'm just a bit taken aback. I'd appreciate it if you could give me some time."

"Of course. We apologize for springing this on you. We'll await your response."

The phrase 'favorable decision' echoed in my head. Like a math problem with a predetermined answer, this problem's solution seemed already decided. And unlike mathematics, the process of finding the solution seemed unnecessary, as the problem demanded a violent, predetermined answer. 'Favorable decision' probably meant agreeing to their terms, I thought.

***

It was not long before I found myself at the doors of 'Soo Real Estate Corporation'. The decision was inevitable, given the predetermined nature of my problem. Though I harbored no grand ambitions in running a cram school, the prospect of venturing into something else was unimaginable. So, the search for a suitable location was essential. 'Soo Real Estate Corporation', stumbled upon by chance, sat in a serene location. It was here that I first met Mr. Denen. He was a man of impeccable style, his soft smile complemented by a subtle fragrance that suited him well.

***

Mr. Denen was gentle yet assertive in steering work directions and voicing his opinions. His ability to offer solutions to complex problems was remarkable, naturally exuding the acumen and demeanor of an experienced businessman. With his help, I could resolve issues one by one, gaining space and time to focus on my own challenges. Even after problems were solved, I would occasionally stop by Soo to have tea, and Mr. Denen always greeted me with a warm smile.

"Mr. Denen, I'm truly grateful for the interior design firm you recommended last time. They were not only efficient but also had a taste for elegant design that I really appreciated."

"I'm glad you liked it. Mr. Genmei is an artisan who delicately balances his designs, considering the street where the building is located and even the people who pass by."

"Yes, I noticed that. It was very helpful."

"I'm pleased to hear it helped."

"I've been curious about something for a while, may I ask you a question?"

"Of course, feel free to ask. I'll answer as best as I can."

"I was very thankful for the beautiful bouquet you sent for our office opening. What I wonder is about your excessive consideration for tenants. It's one thing to recommend an interior designer, but visiting the site yourself, offering various ideas and advice – initially, I was even suspicious."

"Suspicious, you say?"

"I thought, what could be his motive for being so kind? I don't understand people well, but I've always believed that those who approach with a smile without a clear reason are likely to cause trouble."

"That's a reasonable thought."

"But so far, there hasn't been any issue, and it doesn't seem like you're deceiving me or hiding some economic interest. I'm curious about your secret to extending such kindness to people."

At that moment, Mr. Denen's expression softened, tinged with a hint of mischief.

"I'm a bit saddened to hear you thought that way about me. Ha ha."

I could feel a slight blush of embarrassment on my face.

"It's not a question with any malicious intent. I apologize if it offended you."

"Ha ha, no offense taken, Mr. Azumi. I understand your point. It's not so much a special reason or intent, as it is just how life has shaped me. Like everyone else, I started as a tenant in various businesses. Although we now have the Hyatt Hotel and Trump Building in front of our property, I find happiness not in aiming higher than where I stand, but in looking down at the path I've traveled. And by 'looking down', I mean reflecting on the life I've lived, not in a derogatory sense towards anyone."

"So, you mean you don't have ambitions to build an even bigger business empire?"

"Everyone harbors ambitions, and I am no exception. What I often ponder, however, is the desire not to end my life in solitude. What remains for a person after death? If many remember and cherish me as a good person, that, I believe, would be the greatest legacy I could leave for my children."

"Most people seem to share this thought, yet they are more focused on fiercely living through each day rather than worrying about a lonely tomorrow. I, too, am guilty of this, often leaving little room to consider those around me."

"I've had my times of relentless pursuit as well. As one ages, a certain leisureliness emerges. While my own time races by, I find myself able to observe my surroundings more slowly. In forging good relationships, often these connections lead to meeting more wonderful people. This is true in real estate as it is in life—good people tend to introduce you to other good people. If I had infinite time, meeting a good person after another through such introductions could eventually lead me to all the good people in the world. That's why I strive first and foremost to be a good person myself."

"'Good people bring other good people into your life'... Does that mean I, having met Mr. Denen, am also a good person?"

Mr. Denen was kind, with a subtle sense of humor. He didn't tell uproariously funny stories, but his remarks often left me chuckling quietly after the fact. I appreciated his gentle, understated humor.

"Mr. Denen, I always leave here having heard good words and feeling well-rested. Whenever I pass by, I find myself unable to just walk on without stopping."

"It's always a pleasure for me as well."

***

Problems always arise among people, outside the realm of mathematics, yet, it is only through people that these problems can be resolved. My father didn't build fences around me, but he left me with the name Azumi, and, at least, the ordinary time to live as someone who could meet good people. Plotting points in that time, connecting them into line segments, creating shapes to construct life, and finding solutions to the problems encountered along the way, is always an interesting endeavor.

Lost in these thoughts, the expression and words of Denen came to mind, making me chuckle.

"A good person attracts another good person... I'm not sure if claiming oneself as a good person is confidence or a sense of humor."

I then returned to the math problem I had put aside, beginning to solve it again in my comfortable and cozy space...

8. Humility

The second of the six practices I advocate is adopting *a humble attitude.* Humility involves setting aside our ego, respecting others, and maintaining a modest demeanor. It helps reduce our selfishness and arrogance, thereby improving our relationships with others. Personally, I believe humility is the most crucial among these six practices.

In my everyday life, I've always held the belief that '*humility is a talisman, and gratitude is a lottery ticket.*' This means that a humble person can avoid significant losses in the face of misfortune. Moreover, humility is the foundation for gratitude and a reflective life, which I'll mention next. In other words, without a humble heart, one cannot foster gratitude. We must always strive to be humble.

Key Concepts
- The second of the six practices is humility.
- Humility is a talisman, and gratitude is a lottery ticket.

---

9. Exam Performance

Korean society has come to regard the mere ability to excel in exams, prestigious educational credentials, and various qualifications as measures of a person's capabilities. However, I am deeply concerned about defining human ability solely based on the outcomes of these simple tests. Take, for instance, what are the life outcomes of those around us who are deemed proficient in exams? What becomes of leaders selected solely for their test-taking abilities, devoid of character? How prevalent are issues like sexual harassment and corruption among them?

I view human qualities in three major aspects: *character, courage, and capability*. In order of importance, they are character, courage, and capability. This implies that a person with a great character should become a leader. Our society might prioritize educational background, seniority, and individual abilities. Such people, in my opinion, should simply receive fair compensation corresponding to their jobs. However, leaders of even small organizations, let alone leaders of a nation, should be individuals who possess courage and character in addition to capability.

When I look at those who are so-called societal leaders today, I can only sigh. Hence, I respect more the humble grandmothers in our neighbor-

hoods who raised their children well, entrepreneurs who overcame poverty in their youth
to build their businesses and donate their wealth
to society, and experts who have overcome serious illnesses to serve their communities, than the
arrogant high-ranking officials, famous politicians,
second-generation business heirs, or celebrities
who sell their fame through social media and
broadcasting. My personal criteria for judging
people also revolve around these three qualities. I
hope our citizens, in a democratic society, will be
discerning in choosing leaders, not just based on
personal interests but also considering character,
courage, and capability as the standards for evalu-
ating any person. Humility is the foundation of
character.

Key Concepts
- The most important among character,
  courage, and capability is character.
- Remember that humility is at the heart of
  character.

---

10. Living a Grateful Life

Among the six methods of practice, the third is living *a life of gratitude*. Gratitude refers to the attitude of being thankful for everything we have, fostering a positive mindset and behavior. This helps maintain a calm and stable state of mind. Ever since I was young, my mother always ended her sentences with 'thank you, thank you.' It seems she started this practice after she began attending church, although I'm not exactly sure when. But now, as I grow older, I realize how profound and lottery-like this phrase is, as I have mentioned before. Thus, every morning when I wake up, I repeat, "thank you, thank you," and amazingly, it lifts my spirits and makes me genuinely appreciative of everything.

Gratitude isn't something we should feel only when good things happen. If we think about it, we don't always feel grateful when something good occurs; we often perceive it as a natural result of our hard work, not something to be thankful for. And it's even more challenging when bad things happen. *Looking back on my life, the truly grateful moments were those that challenged me the most.* Therefore, I believe repeating words of gratitude can be an incredibly simple way to receive blessings. It may sound cliché, but being born and living to this day as a human on this Earth is, in itself, something to be deeply thankful for.

Key Concepts
- Among the six methods of practice, the third is living a life of gratitude.
- Very often, the things that were the hardest for us are the ones we are most grateful for.

11. Personal Happiness

I believe that gratitude is the most important element in personal happiness. According to a psychologist, "the happiest moments for a human being are when they are eating and conversing with people they like." However, I think that even this happiness is diminished if one does not possess a grateful heart.

A hospital is an environment highly conducive to fostering gratitude. Ironically, while treating sick patients, a doctor becomes increasingly grateful every day. Similarly, having been ill myself as a child, I deeply thank God every morning for waking up healthy and for the life given to me for another day.

Key Concepts
- Gratitude is essential for personal happiness.
- Being born into this world as a creature of the universe is a blessing in itself.

12. International Aid

I personally support African children through an international aid organization called Compassion. These children regularly write letters of gratitude to their sponsors.

In these letters, the children often express their desire to study hard, get good jobs, and help their families. Reading these letters reminds me of Korea in the 50s and 60s. Although I didn't live through that era, from videos and my parents' stories, I know the situations in the countries I support are similar to Korea's past. Perhaps this is why my parents' generation has such a strong attachment to family, influenced by economic conditions.

Despite being labeled as "Hell Joseon," South Korea is now a developed country. There may be class conflicts and feelings of relative poverty due to slowing economic growth, but I believe we should be truly grateful for the conditions we currently enjoy.

Key Concepts
- To cultivate gratitude, we need to view the world more broadly.
- Globally, South Korea is considered a developed country.

The Third Dot: Konosuke

Todai (University of Tokyo) is comprised of a two-year preliminary course and a two-year advanced course, with ten departments that enjoy a considerable degree of independence. The Faculty of Literature has its own sub-specializations within the department, while the Faculty of Law does not divide into departments but operates through courses. Because the Faculty of Liberal Arts Type 1 has many slots allocated for progression to the Faculty of Law, it is common for students to enter this faculty and then advance to the Faculty of Law. Of course, if one's grades are at the very bottom, advancing to the Faculty of Law can be difficult, but fortunately, I maintained quite decent grades and was able to progress there.

Of course, not being a graduate of prestigious high schools like Kaisei or Tsukuba University Komaba High School but from Nada High School, my choice to pursue Liberal Arts Type 1 instead of Science Type 3 was greatly influenced by my father. I believe that every son in the world is his father's son. It's possible to be a mother's son, but in my case, a son was always closer to being his father's son. While one might think everyone is their father's son, my experience tells me that's not always the case.

***

The Faculty of Law at Todai attracts quite an eccentric bunch. While academic brilliance is a given, many students focus solely on their studies, sometimes leading to issues with common-sense matters. Once, I was surprised by an incident involving Tomoru, a student with a strong Kansai dialect, during a debate club camp.

Exhausted from a late-night discussion, we were taking a break. Most of us were sipping coffee or beer, chatting casually when Tomoru, fresh from a shower and clad only in underwear, appeared among us. This shocked everyone, as there were female students present. I handed him my coat and asked:

"Tomoru, there are female students here, what are you doing?"
"Konosuke, what's the problem? What's the difference between white underwear and a swimsuit... It's all in the name we give things, isn't it? The problem is the way people look at it, not my actions."
I was dumbfounded by Tomoru's brazen justification of his inappropriate attire, even invoking the names we assign to things. It made me think that intelligent and extraordinary people always seem to have some sort of missing piece. Of course, under peer pressure, Tomoru eventually put on some pants.

"Tomoru, don't you think it's important to adhere to common sense standards to survive in society?"

"No! No! No! Konosuke! Common sense is just a collection of people's prejudices. It's not necessary to always follow it."

"There's a book with the long title 'Everything I Need to Know I Learned in Kindergarten.' I'm really curious about which kindergarten you attended, Tomoru. This is a matter of basic morality."

"Kindergarten and morality, huh? Looks like Konosuke attended a good kindergarten."

With a sly smile and a mischievous expression, Tomoru continued.

"Rather than a problem of kindergarten, could it be a problem with my father? I am aware of something missing in myself, but I don't think it's due to kindergarten. If we look at it from a psychological perspective, the cause might be in the relationship with my father. I see this era as one where fathers are absent."

"Are you saying you didn't have a good relationship with your father, Tomoru?"

"It's not exactly that, but neither can I say it was good. Just as a father being reticent isn't a problem, perhaps a son not being affectionate isn't either?"

Both Tomoru and I agreed on the fact that a son is his father's son, but I realized we felt quite differently about our fathers. However, this wasn't just Tomoru's problem.

"Tomoru, I have a good relationship with my father..."

Kaoru, who had been listening, interjected, but Tomoru remained resolute.

"Kaoru, that's because you're not a son."
"Tomoru, are you discriminating based on gender?"
"It's not about gender discrimination; it's about the story between a father and a son. There's a special story there. Shall I prove it? Haise?"
Tomoru suddenly addressed Haise, who had been observing this interesting conversation from a distance. Haise shrugged his shoulders, not refusing to join this intriguing talk.

"How is your relationship with your father, Haise?"
"Well, I haven't really thought about it... We hardly ever spoke. From childhood, we only sat together at the dinner table. After meals, my father would read in the living room and I in my room. It was like an unspoken rule in our house, so I don't really remember having warm conversations with my father."
With a triumphant expression, Tomoru looked at Kaoru and me, sporting a mischievous smile.

"See, proof done. I bet if you ask other friends, the result will be similar. Tomoru is not close with his father. Haise is not close with his father. Both Tomoru and Haise are sons. Therefore, sons are not close with their fathers. This is inductive reasoning, like the results shown by statistics!"

Though the short debate with Tomoru ended in a ridiculous conclusion, I realized that many of my friends felt a significant distance from their fathers. However, since I didn't feel much distance from my father, I briefly wondered if I was the odd one out.

***

The father I remember was always busy, but he wasn't stingy with his time for the family. Instead, he felt sorry that he couldn't spend more time for us.

My unforgettable trekking trip with my father in Kagoshima Prefecture's Sakurajima remains a cherished memory. Despite occasionally inciting fear due to its volcanic eruptions, Sakurajima felt like a comforting maternal presence to the people of Kagoshima. While cycling with my father, we shared many stories, the specifics of which I can't recall. What stays with me are the refreshing breezes, the laughter of people, and my father's resonant voice. He was the one who introduced me to the order of the world and laid the foundation for my life.

Our trips to Hiroshima, walks with my father along the river next to the Kyoto Okura Hotel, and watching baseball in Tokyo with him have become integral parts of my life. As a child unfamiliar with baseball rules, the Tokyo Big6 games, a league competition among six universities held at the Tokyo Dome, left a deep impression. I think the game we watched was between Hosei University and the University of Tokyo. The blue and orange colors of Hosei stood out, especially the people in orange sitting in blue chairs. The disciplined movements of men in gakuran jackets dancing and cheering on the stage captivated me. It was more about observing people than the game itself, and having my father there was what mattered most. Though I am now at Todai, not Hosei, the vivid memory of the orange wave I saw with my father in my childhood remains clear.

***

My father was that kind of man. He valued his time, yet he readily devoted it to his family. Every father dedicates his life's time to support his family, be it through hard work, spending time with them, or in other ways. My father, losing his name 'Denen' in the process, chose to live as 'Father' and did his best in that role.

"Dad, why did you always pick me up from the academy during my school days? I saw other kids being picked up by their moms, or their dads would come only occasionally for their daughters. But you were always there to meet me."

One evening, I asked my father this question. He was sipping yuja tea and responded with a light laugh and a thoughtful expression.

"I don't see anything strange in a father doing what he can for his son. There's no rule that says only mothers should do the pickups, right? It should be done by someone who has the time and the willingness."

"But you didn't have the time, Dad."

"Son, ultimately, human time can be reduced to something. But it's up to each person to decide what that something is. Some people reduce their time to money. Most probably do, even if they don't realize it. Capitalism reduces human time and life to capital. But I, for one, prefer to think of my time in terms of 'happiness.' Earning money is ultimately about being happy, yet many people forsake happiness in the pursuit of money. I always thought that the time spent with you, even if I was busy, was closer to happiness than the time needed to earn money. That's why I couldn't give up the time spent with you."

I may be a son like any other. But it was clear that my father was a bit different from other fathers. Perhaps that's why Hosei's orange color filling blue plastic chairs has become the dominant color in my childhood memories. The blue of Hosei is just another blue, but their orange is a color distinct from the blue. To me, my father is someone with a warm closeness, slightly, and significantly different from other fathers in the world.

13. Reflective Living

The fourth of the six practices I advocate is *reflective living*.

Reflection entails introspection, pondering over one's actions and thoughts. This nurtures our self-awareness and growth, aiding in correcting our flawed habits and behaviors. I believe daily self-reflection is essential; without it, our mental frameworks established in our teens may stagnate. Typically, up to our twenties, there are a few people who reprimand us, guiding us in a desirable direction. Beyond that age, it's rare to find someone who will. Who dares to scold a grown adult? Nowadays, it's even challenging to reprimand children.

Without reflection, one risks becoming an uncontrollable monster as they age. It's fortunate if social interactions at work or in society somewhat temper this, but for those with little or no work or social experience, the problem can be more pronounced. Modern-day 'problematic parents' in online forums or recluses like Hikikomori, who live isolated and locked in their systems without self-reflection, are examples that will increasingly trouble our society. We must cultivate the habit of viewing ourselves objectively.

Key Concepts
- Let's reflect on one thing daily.
- Life without reflection lacks progress.

14. Reading

Reading is essential for reflection because books continuously provide us with topics to ponder. Humans naturally have inertia toward their habits, living life as they always have. For adults, there's nothing better than books to apply brakes on this inertia and steer them in a desirable direction. Most successful people I know have reading as their primary hobby, and it's my greatest hobby too.

As a child, during family rituals at relatives' homes, the elders used to say, "To be successful, you need to be sociable and maintain good friendships." I believed success meant being good at socializing, drinking, and valuing friends. However, in the real world, I found that *successful people are often introverted, don't drink, and prefer books over friends.* None of my relatives ever advised me to read extensively and think deeply. Their challenging lives remain unchanged to this day.

These days, I frequently use audiobooks. I subscribe to all the major audiobook services and read plenty of physical books too. On my commute, I usually listen to audiobooks, reading at least ten books a month. As a morning person, I find immense joy in reading books early in the morning, a feeling well known to fellow readers. *There's a saying, "Not all who read a lot are wealthy, but there are no wealthy people who don't read a lot."* This saying holds true. To be wealthy in today's society, one needs to foresee the future and think creatively, and these creative thoughts don't come from watching baseball, Netflix, or YouTube. They are found in books. Books have been the source of my self-reflection, creativity, and drive.

Key Concepts
- Want to be wealthy? Want to succeed? Read books.
- Reading is a common hobby among successful people.

---

15. The Intersection of Necessity and Desire

In school, we are educated about the tasks we must perform as ordinary individuals. We learn that to maintain a certain standard of living, there are specific jobs we must do, and courses related to these jobs are popular. Thus, we study and work as if completing an assignment, repeating the same routine daily as if products rolling off a factory line. Gradually, the thoughts of what we truly wanted to do fade away.

Living life, I've realized *the importance of transforming what you want to do into what you have to do.* This becomes the driving force of life and can even turn into a dream. Dreams should be big. Elon Musk's Mars exploration may seem absurd to some, but I don't think so. It's extraordinary and likely the driving force of his life.

As a child, I wanted to be a librarian. I loved reading, the atmosphere of libraries, and especially the smell of book paper. I envied the profession where one could spend their day in such an environment. Had I not fallen ill, I might have become a librarian. So now, my dream is to build a library.

Key Concept
- Never forget what you once wanted to do. It was your dream.

16. Unveiling the Subconscious

I don't drink anymore, but when I used to get heavily intoxicated, I had a habit of crying. I believed it was due to the sorrow and anger rising from my suppressed subconscious. Thus, I didn't drink much even then, and now I abstain entirely.

Understanding one's subconscious is challenging because the ego always obstructs it. Even as I write this, my ego chides, "Why write about something as embarrassing as crying from drinking?" and tries to prevent me from accessing my subconscious. But the moment I speak or write about it, my subconscious and conscious meet, helping me understand why I acted that way. It feels liberating, like a river of sorrow flowing out.

Years ago, on the happy occasion of my sister's wedding, I drank and cried a lot. I believe it was due to the subconscious sense of loss in 'letting go of someone you love and feel sorry for.' Now, it makes me laugh to think about it (my sister has two sons and is living well, and the youngest went to college this year). Freud's method of 'free association'—expressing thoughts and words freely to access the subconscious—is similar to what I'm describing. *By not blocking your subconscious and following its flow, writing it down can bring peace of mind.*

Key Concept
- Freely recording your emotional flow reveals your subconscious, bringing comfort.

17. Acts of Kindness

The fifth out of six practices I endorse is *performing acts of kindness.*

Acts of kindness mean doing good for others, sharing compassion and consideration, which enhances our understanding and empathy towards others, and improves our humanity.

I consider myself fortunate. A hospital is an excellent place for benevolent acts. Unknown to many, if one is inclined, a hospital offers countless opportunities for kindness daily. Simply treating sick people with utmost dedication is an act of kindness, and treating poor patients for free is possible. Medical professionals know that even slight attentiveness during treatment can significantly impact a patient's prognosis.

Although everyone's circumstances vary, a little reflection shows we can all perform acts of kindness. For instance, offering a warm greeting to a neighbor in the elevator is a small act of kindness. Spending much time in the hospital, I strive to do at least one kind deed there every day. Daily acts of kindness will eventually purify my soul.

Key Concepts
- Perform one act of kindness each day.
- A good soul is cultivated through daily acts of kindness.

---

18. Flex

One trend popular among today's generation is "flexing."

Flexing refers to flaunting one's wealth by posting on Instagram about driving expensive cars, luxury shopping, and eating at high-end hotel restaurants. While I don't entirely fail to understand these actions, they admittedly evoke a sense of regret in me. I believe the greatest flex is not buying luxury cars or engaging in lavish shopping but rather in charity. *The biggest flex is in giving to charity and donations.* I myself have contributed a significant amount of money to the construction of a building for the medical school alumni association I graduated from. Ironically, those who often boast about making a lot of money are the least likely to translate their words into charitable actions. This is true even among people I know. After all, when it comes to donations, actions speak louder than words.

Personally, I have the utmost respect for businessmen who actively engage in charity work. I've always thought that how you spend your money is more important than how much you earn, which is why I see charity as the pinnacle of good deeds. In this regard, I admire Bill Gates of Microsoft for his vaccine and sanitation projects in Africa, and Kazuo Inamori of Kyocera for establishing the Kyoto Prize and dedicating himself to nurturing talent through Seiwajuku. These individuals are not just revered as entrepreneurs who created something out of nothing but also inspire me greatly through their lives as philanthropists.

Key Concepts
- True flexing is in charity.
- Donation is more about action than words.

19. Not Worrying Too Much

The last of the six practices I advocate is *not to worry excessively*. Most things people worry about seem trivial when looked back upon over time. Concerns about children's grades or financial issues are, in fact, minor compared to death or health problems. Even death, when you think about it, isn't that significant, right? Everyone dies eventually. Every rich person, every dictator, every king – death is the great equalizer. That's why I believe *there's nothing really significant in the world*.

As an internal medicine doctor, I've witnessed death countless times. Internal medicine, due to its nature, often deals with dying patients. Initially, facing death can be emotional, but there comes a point when empathizing too much feels like you are facing your own mortality, leading to a detached acceptance. Other internal medicine doctors will know what I mean. If even death is not a big deal, then what is?

In high school, due to severe pain, I contemplated suicide multiple times. However, I never went through with it. I thought it would hurt more than my current pain, and I couldn't bear the thought of hurting my parents who were already struggling. That's when I decided to become a doctor to cure my own illness, and since then, I try not to worry too much. Of course, there are exceptions. Patients with severe major depression, where serotonin function is greatly reduced, need medication. It's a disease like pneumonia. Many people misunderstand depression as just an emotional challenge, which is a grave misconception. *I believe the idea that 'nothing in the world is significant' aligns with the Buddhist concept of emptiness.*

Key Concept
- Nothing in the world is significant. Not even death.

---

20. The Right Amount of Worry

However, a life without worries might seem like a comfortable one. On the contrary, worrying, facing problems, and striving to solve them is how we grow and develop internally. The value in worry starts when we confront a problem and make efforts to solve it. This introspection can lead to new insights and help us grow, enabling us to make better choices. In this sense, worrying can also aid in cultivating our minds. What I want to emphasize is that excessive worrying can torment us and cause stress, so maintaining a balanced approach is crucial. Let's practice moderation.

Key Concepts
- The right amount of worry leads to growth and development.
- Always maintain a balanced perspective.

21. Attitude Toward People

When I first opened my hospital, there was a building I rented. The problem was the building's aging condition, which frequently caused defects that I, as the tenant, had to fix. Even when rainwater leaked from the building, it was my responsibility to repair it at my own expense. I was angry, but unable to move the hospital, so we fixed it ourselves.

Five years later, when it was time to renew the lease, I expressed interest in buying the building. However, the seller kept raising the price unreasonably. I later found out that the seller never intended to sell but wanted to continue collecting rent from us. Eventually, I bought a building on the neighboring street and completely remodeled it for my hospital. At the time, I felt like I was fighting for independence. It was that crucial. While building it, I faced several legal challenges, including a police investigation and fines due to complaints to the municipal office (I have an idea who complained). We even underwent an inspection by the Ministry of Health and Welfare. It was mentally exhausting. However, all the worries I had before moving the hospital disappeared afterward. The burden of rent and stress over the building's poor condition vanished, replaced by a sense of stability in owning my building. Even minor defects didn't bother me anymore. *That's when I decided: if I ever became a landlord, I would treat my tenants as part-*

ners in mutual growth. When we eventually did become landlords, we lived by that principle. We still see our tenants as fellow business owners, adjusting rents to their circumstances and giving them small gifts on holidays. Doing so has fostered a very positive relationship with them. In fact, one tenant, upon leaving at the end of their lease, even recommended a colleague to take over the space, saving us the real estate commission.

The original landlord of my hospital building caused me much hardship, but this led to my independence and taught me how to be a better landlord. Years later, we reconciled. Time had healed our negative feelings, and when he visited my hospital one day, I offered him money for a meal.

Key Concepts
- Treat others with a slight loss for yourself.
- The person who challenges you the most is the one who trains you the best.

---

22. School Teachers

I believe *teaching is a sacred profession*.

It's an important job that should be carried out with pride. However, nowadays, some teachers do not seem to share this view. They regard themselves merely as transmitters of knowledge, like salaried civil servants. Personally, having a sister and a sister-in-law who are teachers, I have heard quite a bit about their struggles. It's truly sad that teachers are driven to suicide by the unreasonable demands of some parents.

Education is crucial in shaping an individual and sustaining a nation. In fact, many of our societal issues can be traced back to educational problems. Our exam-focused education system, which pits students against each other, leaves them unprepared for the creative and collaborative demands of university life. This can be mentally overwhelming.

About 20 years ago, Japan, plagued by various social crimes and mental health issues among children, relaxed its entrance examination system and reformed its educational system. Since South Korea tends to follow Japan's trends, I believe we need to fundamentally overhaul our education system. If we don't address our current educational issues, I fear for the future of our country.

Key Concepts
- Teaching is a sacred profession.
- Education is a long-term investment for the future.

The Fourth Dot: Akiko

In my life, I can't recall ever receiving a gift that truly felt like a gift. Growing up with a mother struggling with depression and a father addicted to gambling, my childhood was always clouded with anxiety. Our family lived in a shabby apartment where you could hear footsteps from the first floor. Whenever my father came home drunk, which was often, the anxious footsteps would start from the first floor. Lying in bed, I could intuitively recognize my father's footsteps. Each thud seemed to bring him closer to my heart, engulfing me in fear and dread. The moment the door creaked open, my heart would sink. When his footsteps approached my door, I wanted to scream and run away. But all I could do was pretend to sleep, silently hoping to get through the night unscathed.

I think it was around my 10th birthday. That night, I lay in bed uneasily, wishing that just for my birthday, my father wouldn't come home. Contrary to my hopes, he entered my room around 1 AM. Awake from his footsteps, I continued to feign sleep. He turned on the light and began to wake me up. To avoid revealing I was awake, I slowly rubbed my eyes and got up. What caught my eye then was a gift in my father's hand.

"Dad, my birthday was yesterday."

"Yesterday? Isn't today your birthday? Akiko, what are you talking about?"

Technically, it was past midnight, so in terms of physical time, which runs from 0 to 24 hours, my birthday was 'yesterday'. But as a child, I didn't fully grasp that my father's mood was more important than physical time. As always when drunk, he began to get angry.

"Yesterday? Today? Yesterday? You're saying your birthday was yesterday? Are you talking back to your father because he's drunk? Now, what? Yesterday?"

His voice grew louder, and my anxiety with it. I couldn't understand why he was angry; after all, my birthday was indeed yesterday. Eventually, my dazed self watched as my enraged father threw the gift, hurled inexplicable curses at my mother and me, and stormed out. Even now, the approach of my birthday fills me with unease. The idea of someone giving me a gift is very uncomfortable.

***

I am quite at peace now. Perhaps because I am dying. I regret being a burden to others, and though it's selfish, I ask for understanding in these final moments. It's a bit suffocating that my last view of this world is from a hospital room, but I'm grateful someone is with me. I can't see well, but it must be Denen, Misayuki, and Tomoko.

***

In life, there are doors that should not be opened. However, some doors open unexpectedly, even if I don't wish them to. In my case, it was the door to my small room during childhood, which my father could enter at any time without warning. The sudden declaration I received was similar.

"It's cancer."
"What? What did you say?"
"I'm very sorry, but it's cancer."
"What? I have cancer?"
"I understand it's hard to accept, but it's lung cancer."
"I don't even smoke, how can it be lung cancer? Could there be a mistake?"
"While it's true that smokers have a higher incidence of lung cancer, non-smokers can also develop it due to various factors. It might be shocking, but if you go to another hospital for tests, you'll hear the same thing."
"How serious is it? What about surgery? What should I do?"
"It's small cell lung cancer, and the prognosis isn't good. More tests are needed, but as there are signs of cancer in the other lung, it has progressed from stage 3 to stage 4."
"Is stage 4 bad? Is stage 1 bad?"
"The higher the number, the worse the prognosis. However, we need to conduct more precise tests. There's no need to be too discouraged at this

stage. If there are metastases, we might consider chemotherapy and radiation therapy, but for now, it's best for you to take some time to process this." To me, all doctors in white coats seemed the same, just distant medical professionals. Dr. Ryutaro, who kindly explained everything to me that day, in retrospect, showed a kindness not common among doctors. However, the shock I received was so great that I resented the messenger, not the message. If they couldn't cure my illness, they were all the same to me, regardless of who they were in their white coats. My mind couldn't settle for days, and I had to visit another hospital to confirm the truth. Of course, the diagnosis didn't change.

***

Dr. Denen was different from other doctors. A first-year internal medicine resident, Dr. Denen seemed almost buried in charts. Always busy, but one of the few who always spoke to me. To Dr. Denen, I was probably just one of many patients under his care.

At Kyushu University Hospital, countless people seemed to just flow by. "Flowing" seemed the right word. It felt like everyone, doctors and patients alike, were just drifting. After receiving my initial diagnosis of cancer and unable to accept it, I too drifted from hospital to hospital until I ended up at

Kyushu University Hospital. By then, I had no strength left to drift anymore.

After undergoing various tests again, I was once more diagnosed with stage 4 lung cancer. Eventually, I took a place at Kyushu University Hospital, with Dr. Denen as my attending physician. Dr. Denen was a bit different. Most doctors seemed either stern or exhausted, but he was neither. If I had to categorize him, he was on the tired side, but always showed a bright demeanor.

"Dr. Denen, you're always so cheerful."

One day, I casually expressed my envy to Dr. Denen. He responded with a slightly awkward expression, one that makes me smile even as I'm dying now.

"Akiko, how can I always be cheerful? But I think I should at least be bright while I'm in this ward. If I act and speak only in a heavy, heavy manner, I think not only me but also the patients would feel more depressed. I'm actually exhausted every day. Just yesterday, I only slept for three hours."

He said he wasn't naturally cheerful, but I liked Dr. Denen's brightness. Ah, I'm getting a bit short of breath. Just a moment, please.

***

Did I lose consciousness for a moment? It seems the end is truly near. Time crawls in this ward. There's nothing much to do but reflect on life. There are no tasks to complete. Although there are many things I wish to do, all of them are slipping away. Now, I just wish for this tiresome breathing, my breathing, to stop. You may not understand how embarrassed I am by my uneven breaths. I always wanted to breathe my own steady breaths. Not holding my breath or gasping for air, just my own ordinary breathing. But breathing has become so painful. Unable to end this pain on my own, I've come to think that life is more about suffering than nobility, more about being led than about making choices.

It feels like my life choices are in the hands of doctors, the experts. Whatever they pronounce or declare, it's about my illness, not about my life. So, decisions and declarations about my life should be mine alone. People say life is more noble than pain, but they often forget that there's a pain that makes continuing life impossible. It's because it's not their pain.

Like my father, people mostly argue and chatter about truly worthless things. What difference does it make whether it's today or tomorrow? The important thing is that my pain must end. I subtly conveyed my feelings to Dr. Denen once. My words were subtle, but my intent was blatant.

"Dr. Denen, I think everything dying in this world is beautiful. There's still some time left to shine brilliantly."

I believe Dr. Denen understood what I meant. But he just smiled and said nothing. Is the freedom to let every dying being die a worthless thing? I'm not well-educated, so I don't know.

***

I can't hear my breathing, am I still breathing? It's painful, but my consciousness keeps slipping away like I'm falling asleep. It feels like I'm almost there. Dr. Ryutaro was kind, but my condition probably didn't look hopeful. Still, I'm grateful Dr. Denen is with me in these final moments. Seeing his increasingly rough expression today, I think my wish will be granted.

35 years, a time that was both long and short. I won't have to stand before the door of fear anymore. Dr. Denen, you don't look well. My breath is fading. Dr. Denen, don't do anything. That injection, other treatments, would be unnecessary for me now. Dr. Denen, please stop.

***

That injection, was it Dr. Denen's answer or his gift? Whichever it was, please tell Dr. Denen I am grateful.

I was fine. My life,
Farewell, Dr. Denen,
I received your gift well.
It was quite fine, the gift.

23. Connecting the Dots

When I obtained my specialist certification, it was right after the implementation of the medical reform, sparking an immense boom in private practice. I had always wanted to start my own practice, to manage a hospital. To learn about hospital management, I decided to work temporarily at a hospital renowned for its large patient base. However, the pride of being a specialist soon faded. For me who was fresh out of a university hospital, the clinical practice in a local hospital was challenging and quite different. In the university hospital, I only had to deal with my specialty and most patients were seriously ill and generally compliant (though not always the case nowadays). But in a local hospital, I had to treat various fields and often encountered patients with minor illnesses who demanded treatments based on their own beliefs rather than medical guidelines. Initially, I was utterly bewildered. Naturally, having only been in school and a university hospital, I was unfamiliar with the workings of a local hospital.

Eventually, I tried everything at that hospital. I learned about different specialties from other specialists and occasionally about hospital management from the director. Initially, I often questioned the director's methods, thinking there were better ways to do things. Now, nearly 20 years into my own practice, I understand why the director did things that way and find myself doing the same. Back then, I often wondered why I had to perform certain treatments, but now, those treatments are essential for my patients and what I once thought was unnecessary has become the spearhead of our hospital's diverse clinical services. *Looking back, I realize that no experience in life is unnecessary. There is no such thing as a trivial moment. Life is a line connecting these countless dots, culminating in the formation of oneself.*

Key Concept
- Every experience and moment in life is precious.

---

24. Values Sustaining Life

Finally, values such as *effort, humility, gratitude, reflection, acts of kindness, and not worrying too much* are all crucial in cultivating the human spirit. These values regulate our inner selves, and through self-reflection and introspection, they elevate our humanity, allowing us to live a peaceful life.

I strive to meditate and implement these six practices daily. Humans, being creatures of forgetfulness, can easily lose sight of these thoughts and become arrogant. To avoid this, I keep these words prominently displayed on my clinic monitor. Let us engrave these six practices in our minds every morning. Perhaps in just a month, you'll be surprised at how much you've changed. I experienced this myself. Indeed, others around you will also notice this transformation.

Let's start practicing them right now.

Key Concepts
- To recap, the six practices: effort, humility, gratitude, reflection, acts of kindness, and not worrying too much.

What Do We Work For?

25. What Do We Work For?

What do we work for? I believe *we work for the completion of our character*. That is, work is *a tool for the completion of our character.* As mentioned earlier, if we live our lives to die with a soul slightly more beautiful than when we were born, we will find joy in any job, even those despised by others. Because *it's the difficult and despised tasks that further refine our souls.* Thinking this way, not only the professions that earn a lot of money but all jobs are precious. Even the jobs people are reluctant to do, like waste management, or those looked down upon, like prostitution, are valuable. If we don't see work as a tool for the completion of our souls, working hours become a continuum of agony, a hell.

Key Concepts
- We work for the completion of our character.
- As tools for character completion, all professions are noble.

---

26. Workplace Life

Most people probably view their work life as a series of hardships. Why is that?

Firstly, because most of the work is done at the behest of others, and it's not something one personally owns. Secondly, it's because people don't reflect on the meaning of their work. Occasionally, I watch YouTube videos showing the daily lives of office workers. Most of these videos skip the working hours, only showing eating, drinking, and leisure activities. This is likely because the working hours are tough and painful.

I felt the same way. Even though it was my chosen profession and something I truly loved, there was a time when seeing patients felt like hell. The thought of spending decades in a tiny consultation room of just a few square meters, seeing only patients, made me feel suffocated and almost like dying. Even though I was a patient myself in the past and knew very well what it felt like, I felt this way. However, the moment I started *seeing my work as a tool for refining my soul*, I felt at peace. I even welcomed difficult patients. Why? Because they helped me cultivate my character even more. Just a shift in perspective made such a big difference.

Key Concept
- "Everything is created by the mind." Let's rethink our approach to work.

---

27. A Life of Poverty

I grew up in poverty. My father was a manager at a textile SME, but 'manager' was just a title; in reality, there weren't many employees, and he was one of the employees working tirelessly in the factory, covered in grease. I later learned that in the late 1980s, with globalization and China opening its doors, most textile factories in Korea went bankrupt or moved to China due to cheaper labor costs. The owner of my father's company (the founder's son) was originally from a wealthy family and had no real interest in the factory. He later sold the factory land for a mansion site. My father, who worked harder than anyone, stayed with the company until its liquidation. I witnessed how a single decision of the owner could drastically change my father's entire life's work. It was a profoundly sad realization. *The frustration stemming from lack of power and capital is indescribable unless experienced.* Afterwards, my father briefly worked at a subcontractor before ending his career as a security guard at another company.

Even though I was young, I made a deep resolve that *if I ever ran a company, I would take full responsibility for my employees to the end.* That's why, even now, I treat my hospital and company staff, and our real estate tenants, like family, committed to taking responsibility for them. I also want to give them the freedom they deserve.

At my hospital, I sometimes see factory workers come in wearing oil-stained work clothes. The smell of oil still reminds me of my father. Seeing them brings back memories and thoughts of my father. Every job in this world is precious. I still prefer factory workers, covered in oil and sweat, to neatly dressed salespeople. I admire their work, their labor, and their humility.

Key Concepts
- Without power and capital, one's life can be easily controlled by others.
- I still respect the countless workers in factories.

28. Scholarship

In my first year of high school, my father's company closed. We lived in company housing at the time.

My high school senior homeroom teacher, who visited our home, arranged a scholarship for me. The scholarship was provided by a jewelry manufacturing company. Three students, including me, one from each grade, went to the company to receive the scholarship. When the company's president asked about my father's position and I replied that he was a manager, he showed annoyance, saying, "I asked for recommendations of poor students." I felt embarrassed; not all managers are the same. My pride prevented me from responding. At that moment, I resolved to one day provide scholarships to poor students, which I eventually did.

Key Concept
- One of the benefits of earning a lot of money is being able to provide scholarships to poor students.

---

29. The Cycle of Poverty

I truly wanted to break the cycle of poverty in my family. According to a study, it takes several generations in a family to break the inheritance of poverty. In China and developing countries, this process can take hundreds of years, and even in Korea, Japan, and the United Kingdom, it often requires more than five generations. This illustrates how difficult it is to move between economic classes. Therefore, in any era, it takes one person to really take the lead and work hard.

We think we live hard, but if we look closely, it's often not the case. Our time is finite. Yet, don't we spend most of it in pursuit of pleasure or enjoyment? Therefore, *unless someone in a family takes the lead to make a change, poverty will never end.* This is evident in Korea. When in history has the Korean Peninsula been better off than now? Honestly, isn't this the golden era? If asked, "Who took the lead?" I would say it was our parents' generation and the leaders of that time.

There's a concept of freedom, which inherently includes economic freedom. In reality, most of us are not free from money. You realize how it feels to be without money when you experience even a day without it. I wanted to be truly free. But such freedom requires an enormous amount of money. We know this, yet we still tend to think of talking about money as somewhat immoral. The desire to break free from poverty and to be free can be a powerful motivation in our work.

> Key Concepts
> - A lot of money is needed for freedom.
> - Be the one to shoulder the responsibility and break the cycle of poverty in your family.

The Fifth Dot: Yoko

"Writer, shall we begin now?"

***

About my husband... The most vivid memory I have of him is always carrying his pager, even at home. He would come home after days and still couldn't rest comfortably for even 2-3 hours, always leaving the house as if chased. The uncertainty of when the pager might ring made him place it beside his bed and sleep restlessly. However, that sleep was always short-lived. For everyone, night is a time of rest and respite, but for my husband, it was a time of torment and anxiety. When he was in the emergency room, he suffered from not being able to rest; and when he wasn't, the constant possibility of a call filled him with perpetual anxiety. He even took the pager into the bathroom while showering. Once, he had to rush out while washing his hair. Since then, he started washing his hair much faster. Even during the stinging moments with shampoo running into his eyes, he thought, "What if the pager goes off now?" Yes, it was a life plagued by chronic anxiety.

In the deep early hours, when the pager beeped, my husband would reflexively get up. But after getting up, he would sit blankly on the bed for about five minutes.

"Ah, I really don't want to go."

One day, I heard my husband utter these words in a tired voice. It was more of a sigh than a statement. Yes, in fact, every time he sat on the bed for those five minutes, he seemed to be contemplating, "I don't want to go. I'm really tired." Without exception, every time the pager beeped, he would spring up, but he never managed to break the habit of sitting on the bed for five minutes.

***

Sound refers to the phenomenon of a material vibrating and the vibrations spreading through another material. Air is a primary medium for conveying sound; when a vibration occurs, it causes the surrounding air to vibrate, and this vibration spreads through the air, transmitting the sound. That's the physical explanation.

However, the sound of an ambulance siren seems to affect the heart more directly than just producing an auditory effect. You might think it's strange for a doctor to say that, but it's not unscientific; it's based on experience. Living far from the emergency room is tough due to the distance, but being close is also difficult because of the proximity. My husband and I moved close to the university hospital's emergency room to ensure he could get some rest at home, even if just for a little while. Like all rational decisions in the world, sometimes these logical conclusions end up being quite illogical. Our decision to move closer to the emergency room was exactly one of these decisions.

The low beep of the pager was distressing enough, but now we had to contend with another sound: the constant wail of ambulance sirens, day and night, which made my husband's life even more challenging. For him, the siren was a harbinger of an impending pager alert. The unpredictably ringing pager was painful, but so was the one that rang after a siren. If the pager didn't go off after a siren, that was distressing in its own way, as it left room for grim imagination. His condition even worsened to the point of developing PTSD from the siren sounds. Every time I saw him heading to the hospital, it felt like a clutch at the heart.

My husband has always been a kind person, but in some ways, he's incredibly resilient. I knew how physically and mentally exhausting it was for him, but he never once uttered the words "I'm tired" to me. He was sensitive to other people's illnesses but somewhat numb to his own deteriorating health. That was the difference between my husband, who interacted directly with patients, and me.

I was a doctor in diagnostic laboratory medicine, dealing more with diseases themselves than with people. My work involved isolating and identifying microorganisms like bacteria, viruses, and fungi from the human body and diagnosing cancer cells. You know, like in movies, there are units that engage in combat and others that provide support from the rear. I'm not sure, but if I belong to a support unit, then my husband felt like a soldier serving on the front lines.

Perhaps due to my professional habits, my observation and diagnosis of my husband's situation weren't good, but he acted as if nothing was wrong. What was that feeling? Or what was he thinking?

***

I'm not sure if I'm doing this interview right. Please let me know if it's strange, writer.

***

I still don't fully understand what my husband was thinking or feeling, but I've come to accept that "it must have been necessary at the time." There was once an incident in the emergency room where I saw him. As I stepped out of the hospital elevator, I happened to see my husband rushing towards the emergency room. Without realizing it, I found myself following him there.

In the emergency room, a young man was lying there. It was clear, even without tests, that his prognosis didn't look good. People were moving around busily. At that time, being five months pregnant, I moved more cautiously and slowly compared to everyone else who seemed to be moving at a much faster pace. It felt like I was moving at a different speed from the rest of the world. But among them, one person was moving even faster – my husband.

He was performing CPR, drenched in sweat. Oh, CPR – you've seen it in movies, in emergency situations. It stands for Cardiopulmonary Resuscitation. It's a life-saving procedure performed when the heart, lungs, or brain stops functioning due to various reasons.

While less experienced doctors or those early in their careers were flustered, my husband was calmly carrying out the treatment. I thought it might be a DOA situation, but my husband didn't give up. Oh, please excuse the medical terminology. DOA means Dead on Arrival, which refers to patients who are already deceased upon arriving at the hospital. Nevertheless, my husband never gave up. At that moment, it seemed like he was putting aside thoughts about respect for life or the Hippocratic Oath, focusing solely on the task at hand and doing his best because it needed to be done.

If you don't treat patients as part of your job, you can't work. But at the same time, you can't help but see the person in front of you as a human being.

Even when you think you've become desensitized, a person never truly becomes insensitive to another. Maybe that's why he couldn't give up on that patient?

Watching my husband's back, I felt a poignant ache in my heart. People live not for tomorrow, but in the here and now. That day, in that place, my husband was doing his best, and in its own way, that irrevocable moment seemed beautiful. It wasn't just about him being my husband; it was about him walking through that time as a person, as a doctor.

***

Ah, could we perhaps end the interview here for today, writer? I have a dinner appointment with my husband, and it seems it's time for me to get ready to go out. An interview for my husband's autobiography, what an unusual experience this has been. Thank you for listening to my story today. Next time, I will visit your studio. Yes, thank you.

What Kind of Leader Should We Aspire to Be?

30. What Kind of Leader Should We Aspire to Be?

In the gardens of a hospital, it is often the first person to clean up after the cats, the one who tackles the tasks others are reluctant to do, the earliest to arrive and the most industrious, and the one who has experienced the most failures who emerges as a leader. In a word, leadership is about responsibility. Moreover, a leader must be strong, ready to dedicate everything to protect and sustain their organization under any circumstances.

I have a fondness for sumo wrestling. At first glance, it might seem like an odd sport, with its unusually large competitors who resemble pigs more than athletes, wrestling each other. However, when one delves deeper into the world of sumo, the narrative changes. Sumo wrestlers, or rikishi, are essentially 'strength performers'. Their size is not just a result of their girth, but a product of rigorous, all-day training routines. Leg strength is particularly crucial in sumo, and the foundational stance known as "shiko" is performed up to 500 times a day, a fact that astounded me. What struck me most about sumo is the respect accorded to strength. In sumo, rank is determined solely by skill, regardless of age or experience. The highest rank, Yokozuna, can be achieved by exceptionally skilled wrestlers as young as 23. In such cases, older and more experienced wrestlers must show due respect, regardless of the age difference.

My point in discussing sumo is to highlight *the lack of respect for strength and excellence* in Korean society. As mentioned earlier, a leader must be strong and outstanding. I believe integrity must accompany these qualities. Such individuals should be leaders, but instead, they are often the subject of envy and jealousy. Those who are gentle and amiable might seem appealing in the short term, but the world is harsh. This is evident even among aspiring politicians in Korea. *Among the truly exceptional and intelligent people around us, who really wants to pursue a political career?* Instead, our leaders are increasingly narcissists, celebrities, and populists, painting a bleak picture for our country's future. Occasionally, I find myself agreeing with Plato's concept of the "philosopher-king."

Key Concepts
- A leader should be strong, outstanding, and lead by example.
- Our society needs to respect strength and excellence.

---

31. Medical Mishaps

I've encountered medical accidents in the hospital. Minor incidents happen regularly in a medical practice, but there was one significant accident. It involved a patient suffering from an injection shock. Initially, the patient had breathing difficulties and an undetectable pulse, and after emergency treatment, had to be transferred to a university hospital. My primary concern was for the patient's life, followed by my family. I spent an entire night in the emergency room with the patient's guardian, shared their ordeal, and visited daily thereafter. Fortunately, the patient recovered and was discharged after about a week.

What happened afterward? That family still frequents our hospital. Normally, patients avoid a hospital after a medical accident. However, they recognize the sincerity of a doctor. I believe *a leader must possess infinite responsibility and authenticity*.

Key Concept
• A genuine heart eventually prevails.

---

32. Go Alone Like the Horn of A Rhinoceros

I always tell our hospital staff, "I consider even the staff as internal customers." Patients are external customers. In fact, *everyone except me is a customer*. My wife, children, parents, they are all customers to me. This mindset is based on the spirit of the Buddha's words at the time of his nirvana, "Go alone like the horn of a rhinoceros." Ultimately, life is something you carry on your own. Nobody else helps. For example, when I am truly in pain, who takes on my suffering? My parents? Children? Wife? Husband? No, in the end, we go it alone. Leaders must remember this fact.

There are times when it's unbearably tough, when one feels utterly alone. I believe that's just how it is for leaders.

Key Concept
- Everyone except yourself is a customer. Go alone like the horn of a rhinoceros.

---

33. Businessmen Are Different

Business is a series of problems, and solving them is the key. In my private enterprise, we produced probiotics. Our initial goal was to create a premium diet probiotic using natural excipients. Excipients are essential components in pharmaceuticals and health supplements to maintain the product's form. Typically, there are natural and chemical excipients, but chemical ones are more commonly used.

At our first meeting with the manufacturer, the ingredient list was entirely chemical excipients. We wanted to use 100% natural excipients. However, we found that probiotics wouldn't clump together with only natural excipients. So, we resolved this by using natural excipients and excluding the most problematic chemical, HPMC (HydroxyPropyl-Methyl Cellulose), from chemical excipients. Even creating a small probiotic involves various issues. Moreover, the Korea Food & Drug Administration's regulations on product labeling are quite stringent. And one must consult with a patent attorney regarding trademark applications. Is that the end? No. There's marketing to do. We need to launch on Naver, Coupang, create detailed product pages, and manage offline sales as well.

Business is a comprehensive art. *It requires pouring all your passion and effort into it, as if nurturing your own child.* That's why not just anyone can be a businessman. It's precisely because it's not for everyone that huge success can be achieved. There's a saying, 'Professors live for themselves, doctors for their spouse and children, but businessmen can benefit three generations if they succeed.' This is no idle talk. A leader must think beyond themselves, considering the impact on future generations.

Key Concepts
- Business is a continuous process of problem-solving.
- Business is not for everyone, which makes it challenging but rewarding.

---

34. Pure Intentions or Hidden Greed?

Whenever I undertake a task or business venture, I always ask myself, '*Is my intention pure, or is there hidden greed?*' Initially, writing this book wasn't aimed at publication. I wanted to leave a written record for my son, daughter, and future descendants about how their father or grandfather lived and what he thought. This writing began with the intention of organizing those thoughts. Ever since I was young, I've often wished that our parents and ancestors had candidly penned their thoughts for future generations. So, I decided to become that ancestor. When I decided to write this book, I asked myself again, 'Is my intention pure, or is there hidden greed?' My answer was, 'There is none.' That was my green light. I hope that my children will also leave their thoughts in writing for future generations.

A leader must always have pure intentions and be free of greed. With a pure heart and selflessness, one inevitably becomes a leader. I believe this to be a universal principle.

Key Concepts
- Always ask yourself, 'Is my intention pure, or is there hidden greed?' before starting any work.

- Consider writing down your thoughts for future generations.

35. Challenges in Construction

There's a saying that with each building you construct, you lose ten years of your life. It's actually true. In the construction industry, it's famously common to skimp on steel reinforcement. But it's not just about the steel. Swapping out parts or changing the origin of cement is also rampant. For instance, the blueprint might specify Posco-made steel, but in reality, Chinese steel is used. The same goes for cement—what's listed as domestically produced on the blueprint often turns out to be from China. That's why, in construction, one must pay close attention to every single detail. How do I know? I've experienced it firsthand while building a hospital.

I believe there's no system in Korea as backward as the construction industry. And my concern is that it's only going to regress further. Why? Because there's a growing lack of manpower willing to endure the tough conditions of construction work. The difficulties I faced while building a hospital are indescribable. In the end, it all comes down to money—a common conclusion for many of life's problems. A leader must not only have the ability to see the big picture roughly but also possess the meticulousness and attention to detail.

Key Concepts
- A leader must be able to view things broadly but also always examine them meticulously.
- Construction is a task that requires a great deal of attention.

The Sixth Dot: Yoko's Diary

February 16, 1995

As the new semester approached, I found myself engulfed in the busyness of daily life.

Last year was hectic, but becoming a third-year student in medical school, I knew my days would only get busier.

It was with these thoughts that I alighted from the subway station and saw Denen from a distance.

We shared many classes, but weren't particularly close, so I couldn't say I knew him well.

However, I sensed an inexplicable dissonance in him.

If last year he seemed somewhat awkward, today, even from afar, he appeared more spirited, almost lively.

A fleeting thought crossed my mind – had Denen always been like this?

Yet, I didn't dwell on it much.

After all, others might have noticed changes in me too.

I had recently trimmed my long hair, which I had grown out for years, and it made me self-conscious all day, wondering how others perceived this change in me.

Had I also appeared different in the eyes of others?

This evening, I savored a delicious motsunabe with my family.

Truly, nothing beats a hot pot dish on a chilly day!

March 3, 1995

Today, I bumped into Denen at Ohori Park Station by chance.

I hadn't paid much attention to him over the past year, and only now learned that his house was nearby, and he often used this station.

We might have crossed paths several times but only exchanged greetings in passing.

When I mentioned that he seemed to have changed a bit, Denen shared that he had backpacked across Europe during the holidays.

I felt a twinge of embarrassment for having spent my break in leisure.

He was animated as he recounted his travels, talking about the people he met.

He mentioned that being sick during the trip was challenging, but humorously added how it somehow made speaking English easier.

The trip seemed to have made him more extroverted, and his self-reflection on this transformation was intriguing.

He seemed more articulate than before.

Our conversation couldn't last long as Kyushu University Hospital Station was just a 30-minute subway ride away, but it left me feeling more at ease with him than before.

Hearing his travel stories sparked a yearning in me for unknown worlds and strangers.

March 17, 1995

A few days ago, I saw Denen at the station, and since then, I've found myself unconsciously looking for him whenever I enter the station.

Though I didn't see him today, I wonder if we'll meet tomorrow or the day after?

The new semester has once again plunged me into a whirlwind of activity.

The school is only a few stations away, yet Ohori Park feels like it operates in a different time dimension.

Sometimes, I visit the Fukuoka City Art Museum to deliberately slow down the pace of life.

I haven't been there in a while, but I feel like this week might be the time to slow things down again.

Of course, I should also drop by 'Cafe Teru.'

March 29, 1995

In an unexpected place, I encountered Mr. Denen.

Having been drawn to an art gallery for the past few days, I finally visited, deliberately slowing down my pace.

After savoring these slowed moments, I headed to 'Cafe Teru'.

While 'Cafe Teru' itself isn't particularly special, its location inside Ohori Park adds a unique charm.

From the terrace, I could see energetic people jogging around the park, though I'm not that diligent when it comes to exercise.

While waiting for my coffee, I enjoyed watching these runners.

That's when I spotted a familiar face seated in a corner it was Mr. Denen.

He was dressed casually, engrossed in a seemingly light book.

Upon closer inspection, I saw it was a collection of Noriko Ibaragi's works.

I don't cherish all of Ibaragi Noriko's poems, but 'The Missing Time' has remained with me since I first read it.

To humans,
Missing time is necessary.
I cannot explain why,
But something whispers so.

Be it thirty minutes or an hour,
Alone in a daze,
Apart and secluded,
Whether napping
Lost in daydreams
Or engaging in mischief.

Like the legendary old lady Samuto,
Too long a disappearance would be troublesome,
But we need moments to completely erase our existence.

For me, the necessary missing time always happens while walking through Ohori Park, or slowly appreciating various artworks.

Now, today, in this place, was the perfect moment for the poem.

Was Mr. Denen's trip to Europe his own missing time?

I watched his profile,

But he kept his eyes fixed on his poetry book, not looking around.

For some reason, his appearance annoyed me, so I took my coffee and walked back into the swift flow of time.

April 7, 1995

Lately, apart from Ohori Park, there have been times when the speed of my life magically slows down.

Today, Mr. Denen and I read books at 'Cafe Teru', passing a path lined with blooming forsythias.

It was a leisurely time, more akin to studying for an exam than relaxed reading,

Neither too slow nor too fast, but an ambiguous pace.

Was this ambiguity due to the time, the place, or perhaps the person?

Even though he's become more active, Mr. Denen, whose intentions are always unclear, somehow annoyed me again today.

April 25, 1995

Today was a bit special.

I walked around the lake after sunset, a bit later than usual.

The lights around the lake started to come on.

As always, it was serene and elegant, yet imbued with a sad beauty.

No matter how familiar, this place remains special.

I received a unique gift from Mr. Denen at our meeting spot after walking down the flower path.

It was a flower.

And then, Noriko Ibaragi's "When I Was Most Beautiful" written on a small postcard caught my eye.

When I was most beautiful
The streets crumbled down
In unexpected places,
I could see something like a blue sky.

When I was most beautiful
Countless people around me died
In factories, at sea, on nameless islands.
I missed my chance to dress up.

When I was most beautiful
No one gave me a tender gift.
Men only knew how to salute
And left, leaving only their clear-eyed gazes.

When I was most beautiful
My head was empty,
My heart was hard,
Only my hands and feet shone a chestnut brown.

When I was most beautiful
I was terribly unhappy,
I was terribly absurd,
I was incredibly lonely.

So, I decided to live as long as possible,
Like the French Mr. Rouault who painted
Incredibly beautiful pictures in his old age.

I had walked through a path of flowers, so receiving flowers as a gift felt a bit special.

But, it was a little strange that it was Noriko Ibaragi's "When I Was Most Beautiful".

Mr. Denen said he didn't want to miss the time when I was most beautiful, like the men in the poem.

I wasn't sure if this was a confession or a literary exchange.

However, the flowers made it clear it was a confession, and so I decided to accept Mr. Denen's feelings.

I didn't necessarily want to draw beautiful pictures as I aged, but growing old together at a slow pace seemed quite fitting.

After all, it's my own imagination, and no one can say anything about it.

I must remember this.

Who knows, I might disappear without a trace in the future.

36. Alcohol and Tobacco

I don't drink alcohol or smoke tobacco. Since childhood, I've been averse to the smell of tobacco, not to mention my father never smoked. Also, being an internal medicine doctor, I'm all too aware of the addictive and harmful effects of tobacco. As for alcohol, my medical practice necessitated abstaining. The nature of my work at the hospital, where I have to see patients every day, made it exhausting to drink. Alcohol left me tired and at risk of making mistakes in patient care, so it has now become a habit not to indulge.

Instead, I have a great fondness for walking and swimming. I've swum almost daily for 25 years, reaching near-professional competency. These days, I primarily walk. Walking, in my opinion, is an excellent exercise. I often listen to audiobooks while walking, and it seems most of my business ideas have come to me during these walks. According to a study, walking enhances creative thinking, and I truly believe this to be accurate.

Key Concepts
- The essence of health management is not indulging in harmful habits.
- For creative thinking, try walking.

---

37. Understanding and Healing as Parents

"I'm sorry about the things you told me yesterday. Reflecting on it, I realize that those who hurt me in the past might have been just like me now. I appreciate you giving me the chance to reflect. Since yesterday, I've decided to forgive them. Lastly, I always wish for your success and health. I'm always grateful for how well you've grown up, despite my lack of expressiveness as a man."

This is a text I sent to my daughter the day after an argument about past events. Every parent wishes their child to grow without hurt. However, often the deepest wounds to a child come from the closest people, their parents. From a child's perspective, parents are almost absolute beings and expected to be morally perfect. But as time passes and one becomes a parent, it's realized that parents are also flawed, scarred individuals. Therefore, we should take some lessons from our parents as cautionary tales and others as mentoring guidance. Even if we don't get hurt by our parents, society will eventually wound us in some way. *There is no one who goes through life without getting hurt.*

Thus, we are always in the process of healing from wounds. Even if we forgive past hurts, it takes time for these wounds to heal. Everyone experiences this. Remember, those who hurt us have also been hurt by others.

Key Concepts
- We are all flawed and wounded beings.
- We are always in the process of healing, and through this healing, we become stronger.

DR. DENEN: CONNECTING THE DOTS

38. Unrecognized Tendencies

There was a time, not so long ago, when my father harbored long-standing displeasure towards my mother. To me, it seemed a trivial matter, a typical trait among women, yet he held exceedingly high expectations for his wife. Once, I even harshly remarked, "Why would such a sophisticated and perfect woman marry you?"

My father lost his own mother (my grandmother) when he was just four years old. He lived his whole life without knowing her face. I surmised that this deprivation led to his unrealistic expectations of women, particularly of my mother. From this, I realized the importance of childhood experiences and voids. However, according to Swiss psychiatrist Carl Gustav Jung and his psychoanalytic theory, this is not the whole picture. Jung explains that the inexplicable anger or anxiety one feels is not due to their own faults but often inherited from the parental anxieties and angers. It's not just our experiences or lacks that matter, but also what we receive from our parents. On reflection, I realized my own fondness for grandmothers since childhood. Even among my hospital patients, I have a special liking for grandmothers (which even my staff acknowledges), despite having a mother and no apparent deprivation. Connecting this to my father's story, I began to understand a little more.

Realizing that our inevitable angers and anxieties might not solely stem from our own faults but from what we've inherited from previous generations can bring some peace of mind. Not everything arises from our wounds or experiences. Let's just observe our own tendencies and be aware of them.

Key Concepts
- Our unlikable tendencies aren't only due to our wounds or experiences.
- Let's just be aware of our tendencies.

---

39. Feminism and the "Crazy Woman"

The conflict between men and women in the younger generation is severe. From a man's perspective, women's rights have become so strong that they feel victimized, while women struggle with their long-exploited rights, desiring to be recognized as an independent gender. Having raised both a son and a daughter, I empathize with both perspectives.

Historically, whenever societies face uniformity and hardships, the figure of the "crazy woman" inevitably appears. In medieval Europe, during famines or wars, witch hunts emerged as society impoverished. In Korea, whenever hardships arose, women were often the targets of exploitation. The women presented to the Qing dynasty after the defeat in the Byeongja War, and those scornfully referred to as "returned women," are our fathers' shameful deeds. These women, who lived and died miserably, were our mothers.

I believe the emergence of feminism is due to the accumulation of such historical events. As mentioned earlier, our tendencies are shaped not only by our own experiences and wounds but also by the scars of our parent's generation. The long-standing wounds and victimization of women, combined with their increasing educational levels, have led to the rise of feminism. I see this as a natural progression. However, I'm concerned about the current societal trend where even legitimate feminism is being dismissed as the rantings of "crazy women." This phenomenon reflects the deep struggles in our society. Understanding and empathy between men and women are needed.

Key Concepts
- Society always creates the "crazy woman" when times get tough.
- Men and women should try to understand and empathize with each other a little more.

---

40. Praising the Great Survivors

In my line of work at the hospital, I often en-
counter people with disabilities. Many of them,
I've noticed, carry a sense of guilt within. They feel
sorry for always needing help from others, and
some even believe they are the cause of events like
their parents' divorce, running away from home,
or family conflicts. They harbor a lot of anger towards themselves, and often, I've seen them
project this anger onto others.

I, too, am registered as having a sixth-level physical disability due to the aftereffects of rheumatoid
arthritis I suffered from as a child. As an internal
medicine doctor, I've realized that no one goes
through life without experiencing some form of
physical pain. There is always a weak spot in our
bodies, and how we manage it is the key to our
health. Moreover, anyone can become disabled.
Isn't death, after all, the ultimate disability?

I remember teasing a classmate with polio in elementary school. Looking back, I deeply regret my
immature actions and wish to apologize if we ever
meet again. That friend dreamed of becoming a
doctor, and now, I too am disabled. People with
disabilities, victims of sexual violence, and soldiers
injured in wars are all great survivors. They should
feel no guilt. *I genuinely want to praise them for simply being alive.*

Key Concept
- Anyone can become disabled. Let's praise the great survivors.

What is True Youth?

41. What is True Youth?

What is true youth? I believe it encompasses two main aspects.

Firstly, it's about having a young soul.

Often, when we think of youth, we consider physical youthfulness. However, I believe that true youth lies in having a youthful spirit. In Korea, students become almost burnt out by the time they finish high school and enter university, due to the excessive education system focused on entrance exams. Is this premature aging of the soul? Most of the young patients I meet are depressed and angry, likely due to anxiety and difficulties about their future. This is also a societal issue, and our generation bears significant responsibility. The decline in marriage and birth rates is an extension of this problem. I think this will gradually resolve with improvements in our educational system and industrial structure, alongside an increase in quality job opportunities. To keep the soul young, it's crucial to maintain a grateful heart. A grateful heart brings positive energy, which in turn keeps the soul young.

Secondly, it's about continual growth.

People often become depressed when they realize or impose limits on themselves. In other words, depression sets in when one stops growing. This is why men over fifty are divided into two categories: those who can live with or without alcohol. Those who stop growing often find life unbearable without alcohol. To grow, one must continuously strive. Personal growth isn't found in watching baseball, Netflix, or drinking. It's about doing what's most necessary for oneself at the moment. Like reading, for instance. Even in reading, don't treat it as mere entertainment. Think about what's most beneficial to you, and read about things you need to know right now. We often overlook the importance of time, but we actually don't have much time for personal growth.

Key Concepts
- True youth means having a young soul.
- True youth is about continuous growth.

---

42. Workaholic

"People call me a workaholic when they hear me say, 'I'll work until I die.'"

Honestly, even on weekends when I occasionally rest, I feel the urge to work. People around me ask, "Why live so strenuously?" But for me, it's different. When you're doing what you love, it doesn't feel like a burden at all. Writing like this now, for instance, would be unpleasant if someone forced me to do it, but it's enjoyable because it's my passion.

There's a patient at our hospital who plays baseball as a hobby in a weekend club. He comes in every Friday before playing to receive injections or anti-inflammatory drugs. It's a kind of doping, and through him, several of his colleagues have become regular patients too. Their passion for baseball is truly remarkable. Even in the peak of summer with temperatures around 100°F, or in freezing weather, there's no break from baseball. They even play in the rain unless it's pouring heavily. I believe they'd play in the snow too. *When you're doing what you love, you never dislike it.*

Key Concept
- When you're doing what you love, becoming a workaholic is inevitable.

43. FIRE Tribe

We tend to think of the FIRE (Financial Independence, Retire Early) tribe as people who 'earn a lot
of money early in life to live comfortably without
working for the rest of their lives.' However, the
reality is different. *In my view, the modern FIRE tribe
is essentially becoming employees of the NASDAQ or
KOSPI in their later years.* If the stock or real estate
markets crash, they're left destitute, like unem-
ployed workers who have lost their jobs. There's
no law guaranteeing that stocks or real estate will
always appreciate. Not working a job doesn't
mean they aren't heavily reliant on the NASDAQ
or KOSPI, does it?

When you look at the experiences of those who
retired early, shouting 'FIRE,' most have returned
to work. After a few months of rest, people want
to work again. Resting and engaging in hobbies is
fine for a day or two, but continuous rest leads to
depression. Without personal growth, people become depressed and age prematurely. Therefore, I
believe that even if financial independence is
achievable, continuing to work is necessary. Argu-
ing that reducing one's living expenses is financial
independence is nonsensical. True freedom is not
that.

Key Concept
- Work is the most important means of completing one's human character, and more than that.

The Seventh Dot: Yanai

It's been over 30 years now. Although we attended Ohori Junior and Senior High School together for six years, I only became classmates with Denen in our senior year. We had little interaction before then, as we were in different classes and lived on opposite sides of Ohori Park my house was near Ropponmatsu Station to the south, while Denen's was near Ohori Park Station on the opposite side of the lake.

It was a time when I was focused on studying rather than forming special friendships, aiming for medical school. I don't know if it was because of my dedication, but I always maintained top-class grades. To be more precise, I hadn't lost the top position in my entire school for the past five years.

Denen was quite a peculiar friend. He shared my ambition to enter medical school, but it seemed clear to me that he had physical limitations for such a pursuit. He always looked frail, and during physical education classes, he was often too sick to participate, his health and stamina significantly lower than that of our peers. Despite this, his concentration during classes was remarkable, and as the semester progressed, we naturally grew closer.

***

Once, I remember seeing Denen getting out of his father's truck in front of the school. The reason that day stuck in my memory was that Denen's ride was not a usual sedan but a truck. While it's not uncommon to see students being dropped off by their parents, it's rare to see them arriving in a truck.

This memory is vivid perhaps because of an incident where Denen injured his leg. He usually didn't participate much in physical activities, but that day, he joined a soccer game. In an unfortunate twist of fate, Denen and I collided in front of the goalpost while chasing the same ball. While I was left with only minor pain, Denen, unfortunately, had to wear a cast.

"Denen, how about you ride home with me in my father's car from today?"
"There's no need to feel so sorry, Yanai. It's not like you did anything wrong. We were just going after the same ball."
"But I still feel uncomfortable about it being my fault."
"My dad will pick me up in his truck, so don't worry."
"No, you misunderstand, Denen. I think it might be difficult and uncomfortable for you to ride in a truck with your leg in a cast. It's not too far though we live on opposite sides, but I think it would be better in my father's car... I've already asked him, and he's agreed."

"Isn't your father a busy professor? It seems a bit much to ask him to drive us until my leg heals."

"That's where you're wrong, Denen. When you're in need, it's okay to lean on others for a while, especially friends. We don't need to be so formal with each other. So, for my peace of mind, let's decide that you'll ride home with me until your cast comes off."

In the end, we rode home together in my father's car until Denen's cast was removed, and this period deepened our friendship.

***

As we had aimed, I went on to Tokyo University and Denen to Kyushu University's medical school. We followed the same ball but ended up at different goals, or perhaps the same goal. I don't recall any competition or rivalry between us, but maybe it's because we both reached our goals that I think this way. Above all, Denen and I were good friends during those times.

***

But there was this one time, just once, when Denen outdid me. Something that had never happened in the six years since middle school occurred during our final exams in the last year of high school. I took the exams as calmly as usual, not expecting any major change in my performance.

However, that day, Denen seemed different, not his usual listless self, but rather filled with a passionate fervor. Maybe it was his passion. In the soccer game, Denen had broken his leg, but at this final exam, I ended up conceding a goal, and it seemed like Denen had seen the opportunity I missed.

Perhaps Denen's presence made my last six years of perfect exams even more perfect. Anyway, I ranked second in the school at the end of that final term.

44. Working Until the Death

Since my residency, I've thought I wouldn't want to die in an ICU, hooked to a ventilator and surrounded by IV drips. I often tell my family, "I'll die working in the hospital." The phrase "working" is crucial here. Initially, my family found it odd, but now they just accept it as it is.

There's someone I respect regarding death, the late Professor Lee, O Young. He continued his favorite research until his death and never lost sight of his duty, even after being diagnosed with cancer. It's my wish to die a natural death while doing what I love.

Key Concept
- Everyone dies. Let's not dwell too much on death.

---

45. Staying True to the Essence

As a professional, I've never seen truly skilled and hardworking individuals around me chase power or frequent television appearances. This disdain extends to politically-focused professor or professors who regularly appear on TV. In an era where the title of professor is overused, this is especially true. Take medical schools, for instance, with clinical professors, endowed professors, contract professors, and professors dedicated to inpatient care. They're professors in name only, but aren't they essentially medical workers? I suspect other departments are no different. The issue isn't just the educational foundations that mass-produce these enslaved professors with the lure of a title, but also the deeply ingrained societal belief in the hierarchy of the "Four Occupations" (scholars, farmers, artisans, and merchants), which venerates the professorial role. Equally problematic are the aspiring academics, the intellectual workers, who parasitize this system.

Of course, I don't dislike all professors. *I have immense respect for* those who diligently engage in research and contribute meaningful knowledge to society, *truly benefiting humanity.* Every member of society is at their most beautiful when they remain true to their essence.

Key Concept
- Stay true to the essence and always return to your original intention.

What is The Principle That Leads The Universe?

46. What is The Principle That Leads The Universe?

In my view, the principle of the universe is *growth and evolution.*

There are various theories about the creation of the universe, but a prominent one is the Big Bang cosmology. According to the Big Bang theory, the universe began about 13.8 billion years ago from a very small and hot point. This point was a state where all energy and matter were concentrated, and with an explosive expansion, the universe was formed. Following the Big Bang, the temperature of the universe decreased rapidly, and the early universe was filled with hot gas and energy. This gas and energy collided with each other, and under the influence of gravity, large structures were formed. The structures of the universe consist of stars, separated galaxies, huge structures of galaxy groups, and large-scale structures that comprise the entire universe. Although there are still many mysteries and questions about the theory of the creation of the universe, astronomical research and experiments are expanding our knowledge of the birth and evolution of the universe. And as well known, the universe is still expanding rapidly.

Conversely, moving to the micro-world, subatomic particles are the smallest particles chemically composed and are units that cannot be further divided in any chemical reaction. Subatomic particles consist of protons and neutrons, with electrons surrounding them. Protons have a positive charge, electrons have a negative charge, and neutrons have no charge. Atoms can bond with different atoms to form molecules. Molecules are formed by atoms sharing electrons, known as covalent bonds. Molecules act as a unit in chemical reactions, where atoms bond with other molecules or atoms to create new compounds. For example, two hydrogen atoms can bond to form a hydrogen molecule. A hydrogen molecule, formed through covalent bonding of two hydrogen atoms, physically has different properties than a hydrogen atom. Thus, atoms and molecules are important concepts in chemistry and physics and are studied in various fields. Subatomic particles, atoms, molecules, and polymers are chemical building blocks, combining to cause various chemical reactions, and these reactions occur in all life and environments on Earth.

From the perspective of human evolution, our ancestors evolved into living beings through chemical reactions. In the early Earth, very small organisms existed, created by simple chemical reactions. These organisms changed and evolved through natural selection, diversifying into various species. In the early stages of human evolution, organisms were created by simple chemical reactions, and these organisms had chemical mechanisms like enzymes that helped different molecules bond to form larger molecules. These chemical actions laid the foundation for the evolution and development of life on Earth. Later, humans evolved into the most advanced species on Earth. Human evolution is not only biological but also cultural, knowledgeable, and technical, and this evolution is based on chemical principles.

Ultimately, we humans are creatures created by this vast universe from a single point, and both macroscopically and microscopically, we are still undergoing growth and evolution. Therefore, we should not go against the principles of the universe. Destruction and regression do not align with the principles of the universe. *Only through growth and evolution will the universe assist us.*

> Key Concepts
> - Growth and evolution are the core principles of the universe.
> - The universe will assist us only when we engage in growth and evolution.

47. What is Eternal?

What could be eternal? Perhaps it's the soul. In a world where living a hundred years is rare, the limits of material things are clear. Thus, the only thing I can take with me forever is my soul.

Last year, my father-in-law passed away. The day before the funeral, as I walked near my house, a blue butterfly, which I had never seen before in my life, circled around me several times before ascending to the sky. It was a dizzying experience. It was the first time I had felt something like this, and it never happened again, neither before nor after. Personally, I still believe that was my father-in-law, coming to visit me for a brief moment. Of course, the people around me disagree.

I believe in the existence of the soul. Therefore, I wish to die with a soul that is more beautiful and pure than the one I had at birth.

Key Concept
- *What if we devote our lives to cultivating our souls, assuming that the soul is the only eternal thing?*

48. The Motto of Life

My life's motto is 'gratitude.' It's crucial to always have a heart full of gratitude. As I mentioned earlier, my mother always ends her sentences with "thank you, thank you." I heard it so much growing up that sometimes I would tease her, laughing and saying, "Thank you, thank you, that's enough."

But as time passed, I realized that these words are truly a blessing. The more I said "thank you," the more reasons I found to be grateful, and the happier I became. Let's always be thankful. *The mere fact that atoms from the distant universe came together to evolve into such advanced beings as us is in itself something to be grateful for.*

Key Concept
- Being grateful makes you happy. Double gratitude leads to double happiness.

The Eighth Dot: Yanagibashi Market

"Wow, this is Yanagibashi Central Market. It feels different from Kawabata Shopping Arcade. It indeed deserves the title of Hakata's kitchen, though it seems smaller than markets like Kuromon or Nishiki. Maybe it's because there are fewer tourists, but it really retains an old-fashioned atmosphere."

Entering the bustling entrance of the market, reporter Kubota found himself muttering unconsciously. It was a habit naturally ingrained in him from his long career in journalism, a way of organizing his thoughts. While everyone has their own way of organizing thoughts, for Kubota, it was speaking them out loud.

Kubota was preparing a feature article on self-made businessmen and was collecting background information on Chairman Denen at Yanagibashi Market. His former lover, Riko, often used the rare Hakata dialect, so naturally, he thought of her whenever he visited the Fukuoka area. Walking through the market, he half-expected to suddenly see Riko emerge from a corner, making him slightly tense.

***

Kubota had built his career by interviewing numerous successful businessmen, so his approach to interviewing Chairman Denen was no different from his usual routine. However, Yanagibashi Market, known as the place where the chairman spent his childhood, was smaller than Kubota had imagined. While traditional markets generally don't have a grand appearance, Yanagibashi, in particular, felt even more humble, perhaps due to the lack of tourists.

His appointment at the market was with Mr. Mori.

***

As he walked between the bookshelves, it felt as though the whispers of books surrounded him. Though it was a small, neighborhood bookstore filled with the cozy scents of paper and wood, it possessed a unique ambiance and charm. It was there that journalist Kubota encountered Mr. Mori.

"It's nice to meet you. I am Kubota, the journalist who contacted you earlier. I hope you'll pardon my intrusion and look forward to working with you."
"Welcome. I'm Mori. Please, have a seat here."
Inside the small bookstore, a roughly made wooden chair, which seemed to double as a step, was placed in one corner. Kubota thought it added to the bookstore's atmosphere.

"This bookstore has a wonderfully old-fashioned feel."

"It's the years it has stood here that give it that character."

"When I leave after our interview, I'd appreciate some book recommendations."

"Of course, I'll be happy to do that."

After exchanging these pleasantries, Kubota began to delve into the main purpose of the visit. He was mindful that spending too much time could disrupt his reporting schedule.

"I came here on the advice that visiting this place was essential while preparing a feature article on Chairman Denen."

"Ah, I know quite a bit about Chairman Denen."

"I heard he spent his childhood here. What was it like?"

"I remember his family wasn't particularly wealthy. However, his mother never hesitated to spend money on books. She was a truly elegant woman."

"He must have been fond of books since childhood."

"Even if he didn't buy them, he often came to look through them. There were these small pocket-sized books published at the time, which he frequently bought and read."

"Ah, that brings back memories of my own childhood reading."

"Haha, he was also very interested in baseball books. Some days, he would stand reading for a

DR. DENEN: CONNECTING THE DOTS

long time, perhaps because he had no money. I remember fondly offering him a cup of tea on those occasions."

"It's clear he loved books. Did you notice anything else special about him?"

"Well, all children are more or less similar. Chairman Denen, as a child, was just a mischievous boy. But he was very confident about his future, boldly proclaiming throughout the neighborhood that he would do something meaningful when he grew up. Ah, Mr. Emohoya would have different stories to tell. He was very fond of young Chairman Denen."

***

After purchasing some recommended books, journalist Kubota headed towards a completely different location. Mr. Mori had referred him to Mr. Emohoya, the owner of a nearby butcher shop. For Chairman Denen, the Yanagibashi market might have been a playground in his youth. Hence, Kubota tried to imagine the laughter of children echoing through the alleyways as he walked.

***

"Hello, Mr. Emohoya. I'm Kubota, introduced by Mr. Mori. I am currently writing an article about Chairman Denen and came to visit you at his recommendation."

"Yes, Mr. Mori mentioned you over the phone. Nice to meet you."

"Mr. Mori said that you, too, would know a lot about Chairman Denen and suggested I hear your story."

"I'm certainly familiar with Chairman Denen. He often visited our shop in his childhood."

A gentle smile spread across Mr. Emohoya's face.

"I had heard about Chairman Denen from Mr. Mori, but how do you remember him?"

"He was a bright-eyed child who often came to our store to buy meat on behalf of his mother."

"Children running errands for their parents is quite common, but is there a specific reason why you remember him?"

"Well, it's common for children to run errands, but it was amusing to see such a small child buying beef. I asked if he wasn't too young for errands."

"And then?"

"Oh, he insisted he was old enough to run errands, saying he came because his mother was unwell. I found his sighing adorable, so I added a little extra meat to his purchase. Later, his mother came to thank me and even brought a small flower as a gift. Flowers in a butcher shop are quite special, you know. That's why I remember."

"Did he come on errands often after that?"

"Once, he offered me a few acorns he had picked up, saying he had collected them for his mother but wanted to give me two. I was really fond of his innocence. I still smile thinking about those acorns in his tiny hand."

"It seems he had a unique way of interacting with people from a young age."

"Yes, he was a very kind and adorable child. Who would have thought he'd grow up to be a business-man running such a large enterprise?"

After talking more with Mr. Imo Hoya, reporter Kubota explored Yanagibashi market a bit more. It was a humble market with narrow alleys, yet it was lively and had the authentic charm of traditional markets. People, he thought, are remembered through books and even a few fallen acorns on the street. Kubota believed his articles, too, would be held in someone's hands, becoming part of their stories and memories.

He had a manuscript about KMP Group's Chair-man Denen that needed to be finished by the end of the week. Before the deadline, he decided to visit Dojinmachi, where Chairman Denen had es-tablished a library. Not wanting to be late for his meeting with Mr. Yanagita, he hurried along.

Epilogue 1

49. "I Hope You Visit At Least Half As Much As You Do Now Later On."

This was what my mother-in-law said when I went to study at my then-campus girlfriend, now wife's home during our fourth year in medical school. At the time, it was quite a shock. I thought to myself, 'Surely, I won't visit her so infrequently.' However, after marriage, my mother-in-law's words came true, and in fact, I visited even less than half as often. I only saw her when necessary, and later, when she underwent surgery for stomach cancer and struggled with pneumonia, I couldn't visit often.

My mother-in-law, who had a special affection for her youngest daughter out of five, happily consented to our marriage right after graduation, during my internship. Our eldest son is now in his second year of graduate school, so it's impressive to think that we got married around that time. I'll never forget how happy she was when her grandson, resembling her daughter, got accepted into college.

My mother-in-law was ill for several years and passed away three years ago.

Her words weighed heavily on my heart towards the end.

Today, I find myself craving the soup she used to make.

Epilogue 2

50. "I Feel Like I Am Being Healed."

This is what I told my wife while writing these pieces. Writing, for me, meant looking inward, honestly capturing myself as I am, and fixing those reflections in words. Through this process, I realized that writing ultimately brings self-healing. The words I write now will remain as they are, but I will continue to evolve. All these writings were both a form of self-reflection and a conversation with myself.

- I dedicate this book to my parents, my parents-in-law, my eternal friend and companion Jeongseon, my sister Eunjeong, my life's driving forces Seongju, Naeun, and Jaeeun, Mr. Soo-cheol Kim, the CEO of Creabiz, who motivated me to write this book, and those in the future who will remember me. Lastly, I am grateful to Something Great, God, for allowing me to exist in this world.

- A portion of the proceeds from this book will be donated to the social welfare foundation "With Asia," contributing to a warmer world by supporting the marginalized people of Asia.